Brain Drain

Brain Drain

THE
BREAKTHROUGH
THAT WILL
CHANGE YOUR LIFE

Charles F. Glassman, MD

This book contains general information and is not intended to be, nor should be, used as a substitute for specific medical advice

Cover design by Jill Little
Book design by Jill Little
Edited by Kenneth Franklin

Published in the United States by RTS Publishing, 115 Franklin Turnpike, Mahwah, NJ 07430.

Charles Glassman, MD
Visit my website at www.CharlesGlassmanMD.com

Printed in Israel
First Printing: October 2009

ISBN- 978-0-9841963-0-2

Note to Reader

The chapters of this book replaced my weekly message. Therefore, each week, instead of the weekly message, I would distribute a chapter. I suggest that you do as my first readers did. Read a chapter a week. Additionally, I recommend that you read it Sunday evening or on Monday. Many have expressed to me the empowerment they felt after reading the chapters and this would carry them through the week.

For those who received the initial chapters, *Brain Drain* is newer, improved, and I feel, even clearer than the previously distributed installments.

As you read, open your mind, and do not believe the nonsense of your automatic brain, which may try to tell you that you are reading too slowly or too fast; that you should be spending your time doing more productive things. Let your mind be your guide—not anyone else and not your automatic brain.

Dedication

This book is dedicated to all my patients
for their trust and belief in me.

———————

To my wonderful children
Zachary, *Jeremy*, *Samantha*, and *Danielle*,
who are an inspiration to me
and make every day a source of daily magic.

———————

And to my wife *Melanie*
for her continued guidance, ideas, support,
patience, and love.

Contents

Introduction

What is it that keeps so many people mired in a bad relationship, unable to break free or to do what it takes to fix it? Why do some people always seem to be sick, or too exhausted to enjoy life? How about you—do you find yourself wondering, "Is this all there is?" To you, does the grass always seem greener in someone else's life?

Maybe you have difficulty making decisions and sticking to them. Or maybe you know you have bad habits, but you can't seem to break them. Why is it that your to-do list becomes the most important thing in your life, the second your head hits the pillow?

When things are going great do you find yourself constantly waiting for the other shoe to drop? When someone cuts in front of you on the road, are you consumed with anger and find that it affects the rest of your day? Why do you find yourself pressing on the gas when someone moves in front of you on the road?

On a larger scale, why can't we all just get along?

During my career as a medical doctor, I have discovered that the key to nurturing the mind-body connection is dealing with questions like these. Our brain runs everything we do; it is omnipresent as it directs, plots, and maneuvers us through our lives. Of course, we also need it to keep our heart beating and our lungs breathing. It is the same brain, for the most part, that has existed in the heads of *Homo sapiens* for more than 200,000 years. What business do we have following a 200,000 year old brain! Fortunately, as you will see, there is a clear distinction between this brain, which I call the *automatic brain*, and our mind.

The automatic brain responds only to danger, threat, or vulnerability. When it senses this, a switch is flipped on and we respond with thoughts and behaviors aimed at getting us to fight or flee the perceived danger. In this book, you will learn the types of dangers that form the basis of the above questions. In the 21st Century, the dangers are quite different than they were for our prehistoric ancestors. An example of a modern-day danger: Your spouse is less interested in intimacy than you are. You will learn in this book why that represents a danger to you, and why you respond by withdrawing affection from your spouse or becoming angry.

The big danger is to believe, trust, and take direction from all the physical symptoms, behaviors, and thoughts our primitive reactive brain generates. By responding instantaneously and automatically to even non-sensical circumstance, the automatic brain can exhaust us, limit us...*drain us*. But by stopping this brain drain, we effectively remove the greatest obstacle to the natural flow between mind, body, and spirit.

In early 2007, I began writing a weekly e-mail message for my patients and many others. It all started with a discussion I had with a patient. He told me how motivated he always felt after talking with me, but that somewhere between our conversations and his immersing himself in his daily responsibilities, the motivation seemed to fade. He asked if I could find a way to motivate him between visits. I decided to send him a weekly inspirational kick in the behind.

As I began writing these messages to him over the first few weeks of 2007, I realized that the issues I was discussing were no different for him than for many others. So, I began compiling an e-mail distribution list of my patients and distributing my messages every week. I had no trouble coming up with topics—every time I sat down to write, I looked within myself and as I sought solutions for personal challenges and questions, I found ideas that resonated with my readers.

I'm sometimes asked: "How do you find time to write?" My answer is, "How could I not find time?" After all, I consider my writing as important for myself as for those who read it. I recognize the importance that thoughts have on my mood, behavior, health, life satisfaction, and success, so how can I, as a doctor, fail to communicate this with my patients?

Most people come to a doctor when they are physically sick. I am often asked what one can take, whether a prescription or vitamin, to stay in optimal health. My response refers to stopping the brain drain, a proactive (if unconventional) approach to maintaining health.

Even during medical school and residency, I noticed the power the mind has in determining physical outcomes.

During my first pharmacology lecture in medical school, the professor informed us that the placebo effect accounted for 40 to 45 percent of most medications' effectiveness. The placebo effect is one practical example of the power of our mind. (The placebo effect or response is a phenomenon in which a placebo—a fake treatment—can improve a patient's condition simply because the person expects it to work. The more a person believes he (or she) is going to benefit from a treatment, the more likely it is that he will experience a benefit).

The placebo effect hinges on belief, and in the last section of this book—"Seven Days to Belief"—I show how fostering belief in the power of the mind is the greatest way to stop the drain caused by the automatic brain.

I will reveal in this book how the automatic brain stands in the way of our attracting into our lives all that is right for us. We all share this primitive brain and for most of us, it still influences our every move. The power of the mind, on the other hand, is well within our reach, and always available to help us overcome this obstacle. Tapping into the mind's great power is how we stop the brain drain.

I first came face to face with this phenomenon when I was in college. I was taking a particularly difficult math exam. I ended up finishing early. As I sat in my uncomfortably narrow wooden chair, I had an instinct, a *calling*, to check the last problem. As if I were being guided by something outside myself, I was led through the problem from beginning to end, correcting errors and finally arriving at a solution that was completely different from my previous result!

The professor later informed me that I was the only one who got that last problem right. More importantly, though, this was my first encounter with what I now think of as my inner guidance, my mind. No, the skies did not open and I did not see angels. But I know that I experienced some kind of inner force, one that can't be defined by the rules of logic or statistical analysis. It was quite real to me then—as it is today.

Before you can understand fully the power of your mind, your own inner guidance, you must understand the dynamics of your automatic brain. After all, this brain is the part of our being that is governed by the rules of our physical world and by the laws of reason, logic, mathematics, statistics, and science—in other words, that which we experience with our five senses—and which cannot explain my college experience. Obviously, the automatic brain is vital to our existence and most of life's events—especially if you have four kids like me! But tapping into our mind is not some vague, philosophical theory; rather, it's a crucial part of our daily lives as we go to work, foster relationships, take care of household chores, and pay our bills.

The automatic brain controls us like an overprotective parent—having good intentions, but forever scanning the landscape for possible danger and exaggerating the response to protect us and move us toward, or keep us in, a comfortable, safe place. In the first part of this book, you will see how to recognize this in yourself. You'll find it illustrated with real-life examples, like the automatic feeling we get when we see the flashing lights of a police car in our rearview mirror or the frenzied thoughts that attempt to reel us in when we step outside our comfort zone. After reading this book, you may be able to skip years of psychotherapy, and implement lasting change on your own. You will be able to see how the automatic brain has been the driving force behind every important con-flict from time immemorial, from individual to international.

Part II will give you a new understanding of the characteristics of the mind, an understanding that will surely lead to a far deeper apprecia-tion. And with the few simple steps in Part III, "Seven Days to Belief," I am confident that you will utilize this new appreciation to stop your own personal brain drain. Once you learn how to do that, you can unleash the power of your mind as the true source of wisdom, guidance, and your true potential.

PART I

The Automatic Brain

CHAPTER ONE

The Brain Drain Begins

*"I never came upon any of my discoveries through
the process of rational thinking."*

— Albert Einstein

Since Homo sapiens (modern humans) developed on earth around 200,000 years ago, our brain has helped us survive. The autonomic nervous system, which is the machinery behind the automatic brain, has been the main reason for our success. The fight-or-flight component of this brain is the predominant mechanism. It reacts quickly and efficiently to danger, with powerful instructions to fight or flee the danger, and thus to ensure the survival of our physical body and survival of our DNA. That was the life of prehistoric humans—birth, survival, procreation, death. The automatic brain is that part of our brain dedicated to carrying this out and is the same now as it was eons ago. Our ancestors knew it as the automatic response that helped them fight or flee predators. Today, we recognize it as the feeling we get when we see a police officer in our rearview mirror or are unexpectedly called upon in a meeting. The police officer or meeting situation are far from life threatening, but as I will show in later chapters, the automatic brain is antiquated, over exaggerates danger, and can no longer be trusted as a survival tool.

In order to begin to understand why our brain is so draining, constantly churning up unwanted, often self-sabotaging thoughts, we must make a brief exploration into its origins.

In The Beginning...

What separates Homo sapiens from other species is the development of our brain and nervous system. Our closest relatives on earth appear to be the chimpanzee; their brains are about 50 percent neocortex, human brains 80 to 90 percent. The neocortex of the brain evolved most recently, and is responsible for higher reasoning and thinking. All mammals have some neocortex, but other animals seem not to. The evolutionary debut of the neocortex probably preceded the appearance of Homo sapiens, possibly around 2.5 million years ago.

Fossil records show an expanding brain size as early Homo sapiens evolved into modern-day humans. Around 50,000 years ago, the appearance of more advanced tools, cave paintings, trapping techniques for hunting, and clothing made from animal hides were signs that humankind was becoming more sophisticated at survival techniques. Our prehistoric ancestors were hunters (of animal flesh) and gatherers (of plants for food). Although they showed signs of neocortex development, reproductive and survival needs were probably behind most of their activity. Their automatic brain still dictated their behavior.

According to most authorities, the last ice age on earth ended between 7,000 and 10,000 years ago. Somewhere between 5,000 and 8,000 years ago, Homo sapiens evolved from being primarily hunters and gatherers to agriculture-based sustenance and the domestication of plants and animals.

Four hundred thousand years (including our pre-Homo sapiens' ancestors) of hunting and gathering for survival turned to agriculture in a relatively small window of time. To grow food requires more advanced thinking—an understanding that something large can grow out of something very small. It requires awareness of more than just the day-to-day need to survive. Considering what life was like for the humans of the Middle East around 6,000 years ago, what did their brain look like? I believe their brain had exactly the same components as that of their predecessors. Their brain was just as reactive and attuned to signs of danger, and able to respond quickly with a fight-or-flight response. But something had to change at around this time to make it possible for humans to grow crops and take care of animals. What changed was our brain—it suddenly became more complex.

How can we get into the heads, so to speak, of our ancestors of 6,000 years ago? The earliest written history of modern man is the Five Books of Moses, the Torah, the Old Testament, the Bible. As it happens, that history begins almost 6,000 years ago (5,770 years ago as of 2009), placing it within the timeframe of the cultural transition I've described. The point is that history from the biblical account places the creation story of Genesis around the time of rapid transformation from hunting and gathering to agriculture in the Middle Eastern nomadic communities.

The biblical story of man's creation takes place in the Garden of Eden. As I outlined above, man's shift to an agricultural lifestyle took place around 6,000 years ago. Adam and Eve were quite happy in their new garden, their new agricultural wonderland. I believe this story depicts the first humans to connect with something greater than their physical environment—a connection to their spirituality, through a newly developed part of their neocortex—the mind. This mind became the portal to connect with an ethereal energy, what the Bible calls God. Their home—now a cornucopia of nature and spirit—represented, I believe, a place as close to heaven on earth as any human being could get.

But just like you and me, and there ancestors spanning thousands of years, Adam and Eve possessed the automatic brain. As described previously this brain recognizes all signs of danger, threat, or vulnerability. Anything beyond our senses or our physical environment is unknown and the unknown to the automatic brain is one of the greatest danger triggers. So, just as you and I, when things are going well and our thoughts drift to the possibility of something going wrong, so too, did Eve follow her automatic brain. After all, the automatic brain interprets basking in calm and peace, happiness if you will, as vulnerability—having one's guard down, not being well prepared for danger. To the automatic brains of Adam and Eve, the garden in which they lived was "dangerous." The serpent is symbolic of the automatic brain and attempts to influence Eve to do something to increase her chances of long-term survival—to leave the garden and stop taking direction from the less tangible mind and its connection with her spiritual guide.

Eve made a choice to believe, trust, and take direction from the serpent, her automatic brain, and that choice evicted her and Adam from the nirvana of Eden. From that point on, thoughts generated by the protective and always fearful automatic brain have forever tormented humankind. Finding our way back to Eden, despite the ever-present automatic brain, I propose, had become our spiritual challenge.

Based on what I know of the automatic brain, this brain influenced much of Bible. This in no way diminishes the impact of the document, nor does it call into question the existence of God. Let's face it, something very big happened around the time of Moses; that is indisputable. I would go further and say that there were many actual "miracles." Those miracles, Moses truly believed, came from God, and were communicated to him through his mind. Those around Moses had to take it on his word that those acts were miracles from God. But as I describe in a later chapter, the automatic brain of humankind quickly rejects that which it cannot explain or comprehend outside the realm of physical reality. In other words, we would also expect Moses' contemporaries to flee or fight what is dangerous or threatening to them; in other words, the miracles.

After Moses' first trek up Mt. Sinai, he returned to find that the people had already given up on him and God. Moses became angry, and the people apologized. Moses then went back up the mountain, and this time he returned to a receptive audience. Traditional Jewish interpretations tell us that the Torah was written during the years after Moses delivered the Ten Commandments. By whom and how it was transcribed is up for debate, even by the rabbis of that time and later.

More valuable for our purposes than discussing those theories is considering how the automatic brain ties into the Israelites' behavior after they saw all the miracles, yet gave up on Moses so quickly the first time around. And this is where I break from tradition. My belief is that the authors of the Torah had trouble accepting what they heard from Moses, who clearly was guided by the connection of mind and spirit, or as some might say, by God. I imagine that every step of the way, Moses met with great resistance as he sought to explain God. Though the people observed great miracles, the automatic brain requires constant reinforcement. God and the miracles represented unknowns, things that defied predictability by the five senses.

What they did see was a guy named Moses, who looked like any other man, with the same parts as any other man, and five senses just like any other man. Though passionate about his beliefs, Moses faced a daunting task in attempting to persuade the people what God had told him. At first, not everyone believed Moses' story. The conventional explanation, after all, is generally the safest. The brains of the Israelites who lived a few thousand years ago were not that different from yours and mine, and we can surmise that all the mysterious goings-on triggered their automatic brains. God as the ultimate unknown is a concept that always turns on the automatic brain and leads to a fight-or-flight response. The authors of the history (i.e., the Torah) had to do something to make God more real and credible to the masses, so not to trigger their automatic brains.

What they came up with, in my view, are many automatic brain-based definitions of God. The scholars of the time attempted to make Moses' spirituality fit their view of the truth. Biblical writings variously refer to God as a judge, jury, king, ruler, father, enforcer, and as something to fear. The Bible contains much language describing both aggressive and passive behavior, which suggests the influence of the automatic brain (I will show later how aggressive behavior represents the fight response, whereas passive behavior represents the flight response).

The creation story itself seems to me an allegorical interpretation written by men who were limited in their ability to see beyond their physical senses, yet had a developed automatic brain that enabled them to think about the past and the future and react strongly to that which they could not understand.

It took a couple of thousand years after the Exodus from Egypt for people to think that the earth might not be flat. (Pythagoras, as discussed in later chapters, as it happens, was among the first, when he talked about the music of the spheres.) In my view, the creation story was created by men trying to interpret Moses' account of Adam and Eve as the first humans to, in effect, find the connection between the power of the mind and spirit and then lose it by choosing to take direction from to their automatic brain. People of that time had trouble accepting that Adam and Eve might have had ancestors (let alone billions of years of ancestors). Not to make all of this too complicated, but I suspect Abraham, considered the first Jew, was the first post-Eden human to go beyond his automatic brain and rediscover the mind as a portal to his spiritual guide.

Throughout the next several thousand years (a period that actually spans just a couple of hundred human generations), the automatic brain has blocked our ability to connect wholly with the larger spiritual force that some of us call God. The automatic brain controls much of our behavior, and although it generates thoughts that are supposed to keep us in a safe, comfortable place, some of those thoughts are distinctly unpleasant to us. Those thoughts, I believe, have been interpreted as people's demons or even the work of the devil. The sometimes perverted thoughts that pop into one's head are the automatic brain's way of reeling you in; they don't mean you're under the influence of the devil. The more heinous or self-deprecating the thought the more likely it will cause you to fight or flee a potential danger. Why does this devil prevent you from enjoying your life? Why does it prevent you from driving relaxed on the highway without getting a thought that you will lose control and swerve into the guardrail or concrete wall of an overpass? Because when you are relaxed, your automatic brain detects vulnerability and therefore you must fight or flee this. To do so, this brain automatically, instantaneously, fiercely generates the necessary thoughts and behaviors. Throughout history, the devil has been blamed for such thoughts and behavior. These thoughts and actions do not have their origins in hell, but in your brain—your automatic brain. Once you realize that, your journey, to understand the power of your mind, will be much easier.

The automatic brain is not an esoteric psychological concept. It is the result of the interaction of our neocortex and the on/off, binary nature of our reptilian and limbic systems—the systems that run automatically to keep us out of harm's way. Any signs of danger trigger this system and increase stress. Most of what we interpret as danger stems from signals learned during childhood. In later chapters, I will explain this extensively. At the time of Moses, that same system, with the same limitations, shaped people's view of their world and their experience. Does this nullify the word of Moses, not to mention Jesus or Muhammad who followed? No. I feel it bridges the abyss that exists between our everyday experience and the often barbaric and antiquated teachings of religious history, as in the Bible. Realizing the automatic brain must have influenced much of the interpretations of God, I believe, allows the vast many who consider themselves spiritual but not religious, to consider some form of an advanced power or force, God perhaps, or maybe our mind itself.

CHAPTER TWO

The Automatic Brain

*"…man with all his noble qualities… still bears in his bodily frame
the indelible stamp of his lowly origin."*

— Charles Darwin

In order to begin to understand why our brain is so draining, constantly churning up unwanted, often self-sabotaging thoughts, we must make a brief exploration into its origins.

What is *stress*? To answer this question, we have to back up more than 200,000 years. That is about the time, when *Homo sapiens* started walking the earth. Innate in the nervous system of our ancestors was a mechanism to ensure their survival.

We experience this in the fight-or-flight response. At its core, that response was the same for the cave dweller as it is for us today. The physical signs of this response are what we call stress. The cave dweller knew only the triggers and the response. Any sign of danger, threat, or vulnerability would cause the release of adrenaline and cortisol, leading to the fight-or-flight reaction, including the symptoms of stress.

Stress for our ancestors was not only good, it was an important tool to their survival. The response was, and still is, automatic and intense. For ancient humans, the fight-or-flight programming was an essential part of their nervous system. Modern medicine refers to that auto-pilot machinery as the *autonomic nervous system*. I call the part of this that directs our thoughts and behavior—the automatic brain. Immediate and powerful, this system needed to be healthy in order to ensure survival in a landscape where saber toothed tigers might be lurking in the next cave.

During the last 200,000 years, our automatic brain has become more sophisticated through a more fully developed limbic system—the main components being the *amygdala* and *hypothalamus*. The limbic part processes information that determines how we respond to threats—i.e., whether to choose fight or flight. It appears to be primarily responsible for our emotional life, and has a lot to do with the formation of memories.

The amygdala, a small structure in the brain, is the central storage bank in this system. Sensory information from the outside world, first passes through this structure, which determines if a present situation matches up with a "remembered" danger (unfortunately, as we will see later, this brain of ours "misremembers" a lot!). Those memories are a combination of preprogrammed genetic imprints together with those added by life experience. A signal is then sent to the hypothalamus—another structure of the brain—to initiate the cascade of events (see the diagram at the end of this chapter). In general, non-humans possess a more primitively developed limbic section.

As we go through our daily lives in the 21st Century, the automatic brain is constantly operating in the background like an anti-virus program on a computer. It collects information internally from our thoughts and genetic programming, and externally from our five senses. The primary purpose is how best to protect us against future danger.

We are all familiar with another segment of the automatic brain: the immediate and jolting reptilian response (as its name implies it is present in reptiles and is the most primitive part of our brain; its existence span-ning millions of years). Gone are worries of lurking saber-toothed tigers. You need only experience a police car in the rearview mirror, going to the doctor's office, or the unexpected call on in a meeting to answer a ques-tion, to understand some of today's "threats" and thus triggers of the automatic brain. The automatic brain recognizes these situations as dangers, and triggers the release of two powerful hormones. The first is *adrenaline*. Its release gives us the immediate tools we need to fight or flee a threatening situation. Adrenaline causes a host of physical changes, all designed to help us survive the threat:

- rapid heart rate,
- increased blood pressure,
- more-rapid respiration,
- dilation of the pupils (so enough light reaches the retina to see the "danger"),
- dilation of the lungs' bronchial tubes to enhance oxygen delivery,
- contraction of fast-twitch muscles to run fast (flee) or fight
- elevation of blood sugar for quick energy, and
- increases of certain clotting factors to prevent excessive bleeding if injured.

The release of a second hormone, cortisol, gives us the long-term tools we need to fight or flee (mostly related to generating energy):

- more-prolonged blood sugar elevation,
- fat storage for future energy needs,
- fat release into the blood for immediate energy,
- if fat is lacking, the breakdown of protein in muscle for immediate energy, and
- natural anti-inflammatory substances.

These systems are very effective, and probably helped humans survive in a perilous prehistoric world. But chronic stimulation of the body's mechanism for dealing with stress can lead to high blood pressure, diabetes, heart and vascular disease, arthritis and other degenerative diseases, anxiety, depression, and possibly increased risk of cancer due to an impaired immune response. For the most part, this type of reaction, for most modern occasions, is usually over-exaggerated, antiquated, and obsolete, as it attempts to prepare us for the worst-case scenario of even the most innocuous of threats. When we end up believing, trusting, and taking direction from the automatic brain's responses, it generally sabotages our intended or desired outcomes. It drains us.

Interestingly, the response of modern humans to threats like a police car or unwanted pressure at a meeting is the same, basically, as the life-saving response that our cave dwelling ancestors went through when faced with a saber-toothed predator. What both have in common is this imaginary on/off switch of the automatic brain. Danger and it flips on; no danger and it remains off, dormant. When the switch is flipped, the hormones are released to enable appropriate action—just two options: fight or flight. In prehistoric humans, the fight and flight were obvious and physical. There was no emotional components, no room for manipulation. The reaction was predictable and on task. In modern humans, as you will see in later chapters, the switch on to fight or flight often leads to aggressive and often self-destructive behaviors for the fight and passive behavior and self-sabotaging thoughts for the flight.

As I presented in the first chapter, around the time of biblical creation, humans seemed to develop an advanced mind with the capability of contemplating existence beyond our immediate physical world defined by our five senses. As I defend fully in future chapters, I propose now – that continued belief, trust, and direction taking from the antiquated, immediate, over-exaggerated responses of the automatic brain serves to block the ability of our mind to recognize true danger and more importantly true essence – our connection with energy and power beyond our physical imagination.

When a situation or thought crops up that causes the first sense of danger, the switch is flipped and we may feel our heart beating fast, or feel a little lightheaded, or shaky. The resultant physical symptoms, which the automatic brain generated instantaneously to prepare us to fight or flee, further signal danger, thus leading to the creation of thoughts as, "Oh my God, I'm having a heart attack." This thought adds to the sense of danger, and keeps the switch flipped on. Without this thought—the dread of a heart attack—the initial response would pass in little more than a minute; after all, adrenaline is rapidly broken down and does not last long, unless more is released. With the thought, however, the reaction enters into an endless loop until the person removes himself or herself from the "dangerous" situation. This is the body and brain working together to create physiological reactions and thoughts to remove us from harm's way. This example of fight or flight thinking in modern man separates us from our prehistoric ancestors. For in our cave dwelling ancestors, when the danger was gone, it was gone and the switch flipped off. In modern humans, even if the danger has passed, our automatic brain still scours its data banks for past situations and drums up more thoughts to help us flee or fight danger that may lurk in the future—the great unknown. And something unknown can be very, very dangerous. Thus, the switch for our automatic brains seems to be continually on. Our pre-historic barbarian cousins had a much less developed brain lacking the ability to assemble past data and extrapolate it into future possibilities. In a sense, they predated us in knowledge of living in the moment!

Our brains will do whatever is necessary to remove us from danger; whether it is the generation of physical action or thoughts. This protective response is inborn, entrenched, automatic, and it's been with us for a very long time. When we believe, trust, and take direction from this brain, we never realize our true potential, which exists in the same head; part of the same structure, within the neo-cortex—the mind. The mind can guide us without the drama and over-exaggeration of the automatic brain. It is what makes us human and separates us from animals and our prehistoric ancestors.

In the coming chapters, you will learn how to become more attuned to this mind and how it connects you to a deeper spirituality and power.

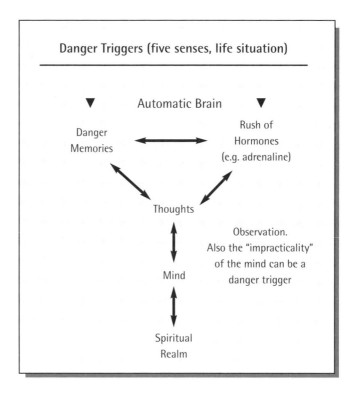

CHAPTER THREE

Stress and Optimism

✦✧✦✧

Life will always throw you curves. Just keep fouling them off. . .
the right pitch will come, but when it does, be prepared to run the bases.

— Rick Maksian

So, how did I begin to learn about this automatic brain (AB) and eventually the way not to believe it, trust it, or take direction from it? Was it a great mentor? Inspiring teacher? My parents? I am fortunate that all have influenced me, but much of my insight comes from being a Boston Red Sox fan.

Now, before all my Red Sox-hating readers head for the exits, let me explain. Until 2004, I along with my fellow members of Red Sox nation, were mired in the belief that we would never win the big one. We had no problem believing that we would get close, but to win it all would always allude us—whether it is the ball rolling under Buckner's glove, or the extra inning homerun, or something; it was and would always be something. The fact was that we as a "nation" did not believe that we could win.

Our collective automatic brains, drawing from past experiences, had us, including the players, believing our limitations, because the potential heartbreak of believing in anything else was a danger too great to bear.

But, in 2004, everything changed. After the magical comeback in the American League Championship Series against the Yankees, and subsequent sweep of the Cardinals to win the World Series, a new founded belief spread throughout Red Sox Nation. Since that time, this belief has somehow aided in a very positive and optimistic feeling, not to mention another World Series (at the time of this book) and a confident swagger that accompanies the team and fans ever since.

The question I pose is this, "If Red Sox fans knew in 1986 that their team would beat the Yankees in the fashion they did in 2004, and go on to win not one World Series, but another in 2007, would we have felt so disappointed, so sick to our stomachs?" Would we have believed so strongly in the automatic brain?

Lorraine is a 62-year-old real estate agent. During an office visit, she told me that the past two years "were a nightmare." She and her husband had developed financial problems due to a failed business venture. In addition, during that time, their daughter had financial problems of her own, requiring their help. On top of all that, one of their grandchildren developed a serious illness.

At the time, Lorraine experienced recurring anxiety, fear, and depression. Nevertheless, when she came to see me, things had already changed for the better. When Lorraine and her husband resolved a crucial financial problem, his back pain disappeared almost overnight–a pain that had plagued him for at least two years. I posed a question to Lorraine: "If you had known two years ago what your life would look like today, would those two years have been such a nightmare?"

While we tend to look to the past for reassurance, the past is history and gone forever. Dwelling in the past and harboring thoughts of "woulda, coulda, shoulda" can lead to depression. The fact remains: No one can say how life might have turned out under different circumstances. Assuming things would be better—and worrying about it—is just unproductive speculation. The truth is, if things were different, she may have found herself driving down Main Street one day instead of Elm Street, and no one knows how that would have changed her life good or bad. Dwelling on the future, on the other hand, can lead to anxiety; the future is unknown and fear of the unknown is the most evident danger trigger of the AB. Lorraine's depression stemmed from her thoughts about her life before her misfortune along with a lot of woulda, coulda, shouldas. Her anxiety arose from fearful thoughts. And despite this, everything turned out fine.

You see, my affection for the mercurial Boston Red Sox is partially responsible for my unquenchable curiosity about this brain I am calling the automatic brain, to figure out why we believe so strongly in it.

Our emotions turn sad when we believe and trust that if only things had been different in the past, our lives would be better now. Our emotions turn to fear and anxiety when we believe and trust the current negative thoughts as if they accurately predict our future. This applies to Red Sox fans, to Lorraine, to all of us. As you read on, you will learn why our automatic brain directs us in these ways and what we can do to connect with a larger power that resides in our mind.

CHAPTER FOUR

The Race

❧❧❧❧❧

"As soon as there is life, there is danger."

–Ralph Waldo Emerson

It was a hazy, warm early June afternoon. We were competing against five other schools in the Millbrook Invitational Track Tournament. It was my senior year at the Hopkins School in New Haven, and my last high school track meet. The tournament came down to the final 880-yard relay (in those olden days, track meets were measured in yards, not meters; 880 yards is about the same as 800 meters, and is about a half-mile). We needed to finish first in that event locking up the victory and giving our team a winning record—a major accomplishment for our school sports program!

I was chosen to run the first 220-yard leg. I could feel a tightness in my throat, my heart was pounding, and I had a slight quiver in my fingertips as I got into the starting blocks. I heard, "Runners take your mark, set…", but before the gun went off, I jumped ahead.

My heart continued to pound, as the adrenaline surged through my arteries and veins. A second false start would mean disqualification for me, and an automatic loss for our team. Did I want to run into a corner somewhere and vomit? Perhaps. Slowly, I went back to the starting block. The sun burned high in the sky, and reflected off the beads of sweat slowly descending my forehead. Gently, I gripped the cinder track with my trembling fingertips. Carefully, I flexed my right hip and knee into the front starting block and extended my left into the rear block. My stomach squeezed tightly, and my mouth became dry and parched. "Runners, take your mark, set…" As the starting gun fired, I hesitated for a split second this time, making sure that I would not again have a false start. Of course, this led to a slow start out of the gate for my first 100 yards. But then my automatic brain kicked into overdrive, and I blew past the other runners. Our team never looked back. We won the relay and the meet.

Our automatic brain (AB) evolved to protect us, automatically, from danger. This is a good thing. Why should we have to think about keeping ourselves alive, especially when we really were not able to understand that we were thinking until around 6,000—8,000 years ago? The fight-or-flight response, and later fight-or-flight *thinking* prepared us in earlier eras to fight or to flee from danger so that we could survive. Generally, in our 21st century lives, though, this response is obsolete, leaving us with the recognizable symptoms, but with nowhere to flee and nothing to fight physically against.

Fortunately, during my track meet, I actually did have somewhere to flee—straight ahead! But most of the time when we feel anxious about a particular situation, the danger is not obvious. In fact, what was so "dangerous" about competing in a track meet to cause me to feel like I was going to throw up?

Recently, while I was in a yoga class, the instructor asked us to close our eyes gently and begin to focus on our breathing. She let us know that we might get intruding thoughts as we began to relax. Her suggestion was to let the thoughts pass, not to fight them—just to let them passively fade away. This resonated with me. While in medical school, I became a black belt in karate. Part of my training included learning about focus and meditation, and we often discussed the topic of intruding thoughts. Bruce Lee, I learned, used to envision himself crumpling up his thoughts like a piece of paper and igniting them in his mind so they would burn away.

Many of my patients have expressed to me their inability to relax enough to meditate. Every time they try, they tell me, intruding thoughts distract their focus: thoughts about kids, work, chores, high school, you name it, all kinds of thoughts that take them away from the path of relaxing. Some patients who experience panic attacks or anxiety even say that they often get symptoms of panic when they are most relaxed.

Envision yourself driving in your car, listening to one of your favorite songs, singing along, drumming on the wheel, feeling pretty good. The weather is warm, the sunroof is open – you are feeling sweet. Suddenly, a thought comes into your mind about a bill that you have to pay, and that leads to thoughts about the vendor you need to pay, who might remind you of someone you knew in high school, who was on your team, and the team lost an important game…and the negative thoughts rage on, taking you from that good place. Suddenly, you may not feel so good at all. Or what about the brief anxiety you may experience because of a sudden, out of nowhere thought that you may somehow lose control, swerve and smash into the guardrail or overpass?

What had been instilling fear in me in my high school race? What was my brain interpreting as dangerous? The other runners on my team did not seem as nervous as I was…or were they? How can fear of danger intrude when you've been feeling good driving in your car, or trying to relax? The fact is, *what constitutes danger for one person is different for another*. Perhaps for me, success was the danger. Relaxation for everyone is an act that the AB interprets as having our guard down. Any negative thought that pops into your head while you are feeling good or relaxed is your AB's attempt to help you flee or fight this potentially "dangerous" circumstance.

In the next few chapters, you will see from where these danger triggers arise.

CHAPTER FIVE

Our Childish Brain

❧❀❧

*"So, like a forgotten fire, a childhood can always
flare up again within us."*

–Gaston Bachelard

A t around 1:30 p.m. on November 22, 1963, little three-year-old, almost-four-year-old, me, played in the small living area of a two-bedroom apartment in the Northeast section of Washington, DC, (the city of my birth and first few years of life). Suddenly, my mother ran into the room clutching her head and screaming, "Oh my God, President Kennedy's been shot!" Just about the same time, through the open door of our patio, I heard an ambulance go by. For too many years than I wish to admit, I made an association that I had heard President Kennedy's ambulance en route to the hospital. Of course, I learned at some point that the assassination occurred in Dallas, not Washington. However, living in Washington and having close relatives closely involved in the Administration, I know there must have been much talk about Kennedy—enough for an almost-four-year-old to recall. So I carried this memory with me for a long time.

Although nerve-cell connections are made and broken throughout our lives, at no time does the frequency and magnitude exceed what inundates us during our first twelve to thirteen years. These youthful connections form the memories we later call upon to determine what is dangerous. Often these memories have nothing to do with reality, as the connections are laid down in a hodgepodge way (Kennedy shot, ambulance heard, must have been Kennedy's ambulance). Before our minds can reach such logical conclusions as that if A = B, and B = C, then A = C, the raw connection is made and firmly affixed in our bank of danger memories. Unfortunately, the fact remains that when we are old enough to make such conclusions, our AB calls upon these memories, which confound logic and often make no sense with our present reality (for instance, why should you feel nervous about pointing out to the deli clerk that you asked for your turkey sandwich with mustard, not mayo).

Many triggers to our automatic brain have their origin in our younger years. These memories form the foundation of what we will call upon to determine what is dangerous. Though my early experience with hearing the ambulance was not necessarily a memory of danger, it exemplifies a false association and provides a glimpse into this dynamic.

My earliest memory of feeling the fight-or-flight response was in second grade. After exchanging Valentine's Day cards in school, I took home a very special one from a girl in the class on whom, my parents later told me, I had a crush. I don't remember everything about this incident, but I remember clearly that my mother encouraged me to call her on the telephone, to thank her. I did not want to, but Mom pushed.

As I slowly dialed (yes, with an actual dial) the number, my heart was pounding. Today, these many years later, I confess that I do not remember anything about the conversation, but it couldn't have made much of an impression on the girl; I saw her years later and she did not have a recollection either. What I do remember is the pounding of my heart. I did not share this with my mother, nor did I have any accompanying thoughts of impending doom. Nevertheless, at the tender age of seven, it's clear that I already harbored a danger memory, and it connected this act with something dangerous; enough to cause my automatic brain to react in a fashion preparing me to fight or flee this "grave danger".

At this point, you may be thinking, "What was there to worry about? The worst she could say was no." As I entered dating age, I heard this statement a lot! So why *did* asking someone out on a date cause such anxiety? Apparently, for me (and no doubt for many others) this represented a dangerous activity. The fight-or-flight reaction gets mixed up with fears that she might say more than a simple no—things like, "Why would I go out with the likes of *you*? I wouldn't be seen in the same city as you! Why would I go out with a loser like *you*?!"

That kind of cruelty rarely happens, but that fact doesn't stop the automatic brain from preparing us from this worst-case scenario. A scenario that would place us in the vulnerable position of embarrassment, and since danger, threat, or vulnerability triggers our AB, it is not surprising that we might feel the effects.

Our automatic brain, always trying to help us survive in the jungle, will do whatever is necessary to remove us from harm's way or prepare us to fight. For in the jungle, if one shows weakness, vulnerability, or others are viewed as superior, the extreme could mean life or death. Dramatic? Perhaps. But this is the way our AB operates.

Calling my classmate got automatically associated with danger due to the web of neural synapses already laid down in my automatic brain. Since many of these kinds of connections arise prior to adolescence, our adult actions and thought processes may be similar to those of an adolescent or pre-adolescent. A pretty scary presumption; however, it plays out over and over again in our adult lives.

Often the connections in our brain are based on more than one event or one instance. I have recently worked with a sixty-year-old woman named Jane who has struggled for many years with her weight. Jane confided to me that she was frustrated and had given up on her efforts to lose weight. After all, she explained, "What if you were told that if you studied more and more you would get better grades on tests, so you studied more and more and you still got lousy grades?" That is how she feels about trying to lose weight.

Every time Jane attempted to become fit or even visualize herself as a fit person, her good intentions would automatically be sabotaged by destructive behaviors or thoughts. With each new initiative, she would get thoughts like, "Why am I doing this, it's not going to work anyway, never does, never will. Why am I starving myself?" Though she kept trying, the thoughts were always there in the background.

I suspected that no one event was at the heart of her repeated failures. Rather, I suspected that somewhere during her childhood she had stored, as a "dangerous" memory, the idea of being a thin, vibrant, healthy, sexy, free, independent person—the essence of what she viewed as her inner goddess. She initially resisted this idea, but then, during the last five minutes of our second meeting, she began to recall events that had occurred when she was eight years old. During that year, she was sick with pneumonia and she lost ten pounds. She said that she distinctly remembers her grandparents hovering over her and, in their eastern European accents, cajoling her, "You're too thin! You have to eat, you have to eat!" And her mother also chiming in, "You have to eat, you have to eat!"

Jane went on to ask, "If I can identify it and understand it cognitively, why can't I say 'that was then, this is now'?" I explained that the reason is that the atmosphere in her home during the time she was sick had created her danger memory. Her neurons became locked in and permanently connected. Her actual conscious memory was of her relatives hovering over her once or twice and uttering those words, but what had locked in the danger memory so profoundly was the atmosphere around the home at the time she was sick.

The smells that were around during that time, the discussions around the house, everything was affected by the needs of a very sick child who was losing weight and needed to be nursed back to health. The details are less important than the understanding that these danger memories—as silly as they may seem now to an adult, rational mind—serve as the stimulus for the automatic brain's protective response. Its gears go into motion and it generates thoughts and actions designed to pull us into a comfortable, safe area. For Jane, the danger area is the prospect of being thin, and her automatic brain fires on all cylinders to pull her back. It doesn't matter that this response by the automatic brain is in direct opposition to what her adult, rational brain wants.

The first step in mastering your automatic brain is accepting that there are stored memories, perhaps haphazard and illogical, that fuel it.

CHAPTER SIX

Independence – An Unlikely Suspect

"If you are distressed by anything external, the pain is not due to the thing itself, but to your estimate of it; and this you have the power to revoke at any moment."

-Marcus Aurelius

When Albert Einstein first came to Princeton University in 1933, he was invited into a classroom to meet with the Mathematics Department chairman. The chairman was furiously working on a difficult proof, one of which he was especially proud. As he wrote quickly, Einstein interrupted in a quiet voice, "Excuse me, but could you please work a little more slowly? I was never really very good in math." Einstein was later quoted as saying, "Do not worry about your problems with mathematics; I assure you mine are far greater."

Toward the end of my second year of medical school, I prepared for the first of my large board exams. One day while I studied, I felt my pulse and detected what seemed like a skipped beat. Even though by this time I was supposed to be an "expert" at diagnosis, I asked my roommate to take my blood pressure. He got 130 over 80, well within a normal range and certainly no reason to raise concern. However, earlier that year, when we were learning how to take blood pressure measurements, mine had never exceeded 120/80, which is regarded as normal. This new reading fed into my medical-school-syndrome paranoia—I was now developing high blood pressure and premature heart disease.

That weekend, I visited my parents and could not hide my anxiety about this "high" blood pressure and the "palpitations" I had detected. As it happens, one of my mother's greatest fears was that her son would suffer the same fate as her father and brother: both had died of heart attacks in their 40s. I was whisked off first to an internist and then to a cardiologist. The former found my blood pressure even a little higher, and proceeded to scare the crap out of me by suggesting I be tested for a *pheochromocytoma* (a tumor that secretes adrenaline). Needless to say he was not familiar with the automatic brain! The cardiologist found my pulse elevated and my blood pressure 140/90. But at least he tried not to scare me, explaining that this was typical medical-school-syndrome, exacerbated by my studying for the boards. He told me not to worry and to forget about it.

Great advice, but the fact is that this particular 23-year-old soon-to-be doctor possessed a fairly robust automatic brain. These events triggered danger memories on several different levels (about which to I will discuss later). Instead of taking the cardiologist's advice, my parents and I decided that I would see one of the leading experts in hypertension. In his consultation office was a large mahogany desk, behind which he sat in his white coat, glasses, and very serious expression. I sat in front, a little to the side with an electric blood pressure cuff attached to my arm, which was resting on a side table. Every few seconds, as the doctor took my history, the cuff would tighten around my arm with a deep, vibrating, almost rumbling sound. And each time I felt my heart race and felt my body tremble. My danger memories were being reinforced, and I was experiencing a classic case of "white-coat syndrome"—the phenomenon that often drives people's blood pressure up just because it's being taken by a doctor in a stressful environment.

In part, this experience propelled me on my quest to understand the automatic brain. I believe it has also made me a more understanding physician. Just as Einstein could understand a student's struggles with math, I can completely empathize with my patients who fear doctors.

But years would pass until I began to work out fully the dynamic of the automatic brain.

The triggers of the automatic brain, the dangers, differ for everyone. Nevertheless, there exist a few universal triggers. As children, we are dependent on parents and other caretakers for our survival needs. Leaving this childhood safety net introduces danger, a threat to our survival. Our immature, automatic brain begins to conjure up danger memories very early on, and to create a host of related nervous connections. Instead of being purely a liberating experience, any situation that brings us closer to independence—to our ability to soar high, to leave the nest, to break free from our parents—is scary for a child. A child's developing brain locks in this freedom as potential danger and stores it as a danger memory, thus the process of leaving our comfort zone is forever linked, even if only subconsciously, to danger and a threat to survival.

As adults, all of this helps explain why the automatic brain fills our heads with negative, limiting thoughts when we try to leave whatever comfort zone we're in at the moment, and any time we strive to be free and independent. For many adults, the act of asserting a point of view or expressing a personal need is difficult for this very reason. Doing those things represents an effort to gain independence, and can trigger the automatic brain to fire. Many patients have confided to me that they hate confrontation because it causes them to have uncomfortable thoughts or even actual physical discomfort. In confrontational situations, the automatic brain triggers and the fight-or-flight behaviors and thoughts follow.

Einstein had an automatic brain, just like you and me. When confronted with that stressful mathematics situation, he could have been passive and not confronted the professor with his confusion—the "flight" option. Or he could have reacted by being aggressive and bullying the professor, invoking his stature as a world-renowned physicist—the "fight" option. Both types of reactions are largely automatic, and arise from the subconscious danger memories of what happens if we leave the nest. Einstein may have taken direction, though, from his higher mind, (which I will discuss at length in the second part of this book), and been assertive—neither fighting nor fleeing.

The universal triggers of independence, confrontation, and as I will describe later the trigger of being "one-upped", played a role also in my early medical experience, and they in fact play a crucial role in explaining why most people do not like to go to doctors. Doctors represent authority figures, ones we're not easily able to confront, and who seem to be superior to us. But a productive doctor-patient relationship calls upon the patient to be an active participant—in other words, to become independent, not subservient, thus potentially leading to a trigger of the patient's automatic brain. Thus, an automatic response to this threat is to avoid doctors completely—to flee the "danger" by avoiding it, or to take everything the doctor says as gospel without questioning, even though some of it may not seem right in your gut.

The other automatic response is to "fight" the danger through aggressive posturing, a confrontational attitude, anger, and sometimes threats—perhaps to leave and get another doctor or threaten a lawsuit. Both are automatic responses generated by the same universal triggers. Back in my med school situation, I chose a passive response, following the direction my automatic brain laid out. I had listened to whatever the first doctor said, asking no questions. Rather than leaving the nest, I went home to enlist my parents in the process.

The act of calling my classmate that I discussed in the previous chapter represented an independent act. Already by the tender age of seven, the danger memory inspired by that act fueled the release of adrenaline for a purely physical reaction. The automatic brain can generate a purely physical response or generate thoughts that direct our behavior to fight or flee the perceived danger.

Generally, and understandably, the atmosphere around young children is protective. Even so, as a child's brain develops, a number of danger memories lock in place, automatically and haphazardly. And that doesn't mean that parenting is to blame for the child's exposure to perceived danger. You should not interpret my statements here as any kind of indictment of caring, well-intentioned parents. The fact is that even with the best parenting, danger memories get linked to independent activities as adults and can serve to trigger the automatic brain and fight-or-flight thinking or physical reaction. The physical and mental responses of this automatic system can be so uncomfortable that they reinforce the need to react to these independent activities. Thoughts creep in, and cause most people either to retreat by acting passively, or to fight by acting aggressively.

There is another, more insidious way in which the comfort of "the nest" serves as the basis of a danger memory worthy of flipping on the automatic brain's switch. Since the strong connections among brain cells are formed in our early years, as adults we carry in our head a child's brain, wired to alert us when we venture into uncharted—dangerous, unknown—territory. Now, suppose your "nest" as a child (i.e. what was familiar to you) was occupied by parents with hang-ups about money or cared little about their health, or had mental illness, for example. Then the opposite of those things—financial security, or a healthy and fit body, or even emotional stability—would be unknown or unfamiliar.

Do you now wonder why, as an adult, you constantly find yourself in bad relationships, or broke, or overweight? Does your life seem to automatically self-sabotage when things are going well? I strongly believe that all the good stuff in our lives can actually act as a danger trigger that flips on the automatic brain, if your growing up "nest" was as the one above. The good stuff is unfamiliar, unknown, and hence dangerous to the childish automatic brain. The unhappiness and confusion is what formed your AB's connections, and it is locked in as being familiar.

The AB's biggest fear is the unknown. Whenever, as an adult, you drift into these "unknown, unfamiliar" areas, the trigger goes off and you automatically fight or flee. You might "flee" by avoiding stable relationships or relationships altogether, disdaining money—perceiving it as evil, or ignoring your health. The "fight" could take the form of anger, rage, or envy toward people who have those things, or self-destructive behavior like gambling and excessive eating. It might even show up as physical or psychological abuse of others, or of yourself.

Because these responses happen automatically and are typically quite distressing, they can bring on feelings of loss of control. Before I figured this out, I too felt that I was losing control every time someone came at me with a blood-pressure cuff. The fight-or-flight thinking and physical symptoms would kick in. This sense of lack of control leads some people to self-medicate with alcohol or drugs—they're trying to calm the automatic brain. It's why you may feel the need to calm your nerves by having a drink before you go to a party where you'll be meeting lots of people for the first time.

It's important to realize that these triggers are universal, and entirely normal—human. But most people don't share their feelings with others, so they tend to think they're the only ones who feel this way. That reinforces the sense of not being in control and can lead to chronic stress and pessimism. If it gets worse, it can bring on chronic anxiety or depression.

Who would think that the uncomfortable could be perceived as safer? Such is the irony of the automatic brain and its many danger triggers. These triggers cannot be believed, trusted, or used to guide us.

The fact is that our attempts to achieve independence will always trigger, to some extent, our AB as we venture beyond our comfort zone—no matter how discomforting the "comfort" zone really is. Understanding this will bring you closer to gaining control over the greatest limitation on your life. We must not believe, trust, or take direction from the AB's activity. Accepting this concept will stop your AB from defining and shaping your thoughts and actions.

CHAPTER SEVEN

What's Love Got to Do with It?

✦❈✦

"Love is like oxygen,
You get too much you get too high,
Not enough and you're gonna die ...."

—Sweet (1978)

Phyllis is a 48-year-old mother of two.

Phyllis: Dr. G, no matter how hard I try, I continue to struggle with my weight. When I was married, I was 125 pounds, and now I am 200 pounds. I really don't eat that much, but sometimes I just feel like I have no control—something just takes over.

Dr. G: That sounds very frustrating, Phyllis. Generally, when people feel they're not in control, it is because their automatic brain is directing their behavior.

Phyllis: What does that mean?

Dr. G: Our automatic brain functions solely to protect us from danger, to generate thoughts and actions that drive us from a place of danger to one of safety.

Phyllis: Dr. Glassman, I'm still not sure I understand what that has to do with my predicament.

Dr. G: You are listening to your automatic brain, and what it is telling you, is that somehow being overweight is a safer place for you than weighing 125 pounds. I know that may sound a little implausible, but let me ask you a few questions to try to get at the root of this: What was the atmosphere around your house when you were growing up? Do you recall any incidents involving weight issues?

Phyllis: I do remember a few things. When I was growing up, my mother always commented on my appearance. If I dressed up or put on makeup—when I was older—or looked at myself in the mirror, she would say, "Stop showing off!" If I bought something for myself she would say, "You're so selfish!" I always probably had a distorted body image, thinking I looked fat even though I was thin. My mother was heavy when I was growing up and in some ways I think she envied me.

Tom is 35 years old, married and father of a newborn, and CEO of a successful business.

Tom: Dr. G, I am sick and tired of feeling sick all the time. It seems like every few months it's something else. Almost every day I wake up with a headache, and I am having a hard time sleeping. The problem is that I have some stupid little things that make me anxious, that someone else who is calm and relaxed might look forward to.

Dr. G: I understand fully, Tom. Everyone is different and everyone's data banks of danger memories are different. The specific "stupid" events are less important than the realization that they are the trigger for your automatic brain to go on a wild data-search to protect you. The search comes up with anything and everything to pull you away from these events, and often points to the root associations formed in your childhood. The current events are somehow associated with danger because of the information that's stored in the data banks. The fact is, for every little event that may be disruptive to you, there is a larger, hidden trigger.

Tom: I used to think that I was in control of my thoughts, that they were me—I was my thoughts. Now I feel they are controlling me, and almost not a part of me.

Dr. G: The thoughts you do not feel are part of you but that are controlling you—they are merely surges of electrical impulses as your nerve cells talk to one another resulting in thoughts. These are part of the automatic brain and appear spontaneously; much like the physical response you get when you are startled or when you suddenly see the flashing lights of a police car in your rearview mirror. The reason you feel you don't have control over them is because…you don't. The thoughts are part of the protective response that goes back 6,000—8,000 years and a response to being startled that goes back more than 200,000 years. As you might imagine, by now it is solidly imprinted in our brain. It will always be with you. Awareness of this is the first step in developing adaptive behaviors to deal with it.

An example I like to use is from the film A Beautiful Mind. Russell Crowe plays the brilliant mathematician, John Forbes Nash. Nash suffered from schizophrenia, which is far from what you are experiencing. Nash saw and heard delusions, but later in life he was able to recognize that these delusions were not real. In his later years, as he strolled the campus of Princeton University, his three main delusionary figures—a small girl, a college friend, and an FBI agent—walked along side him, chatting with him as they did his entire life. The difference was that by this time he no longer believed them, trusted them, or took directions from them.

It is important to acknowledge the automatic brain, and I will show you strategies to keep it in its place—in other words, to help you not believe it, or trust it, or continually take direction from it.

Tom: That makes total sense to me. I just don't understand why all of a sudden I started getting these stupid thoughts, and where they are coming from.

Dr. G: One of the strongest triggers for many people is the notion that striving for independence triggers the automatic brain, you guessed it, automatically. However, there are several other universal triggers. Do you recall how your family treated the discussion of health? How about money—what was the overall feeling around your home while you were growing up about money and those who had more money than your family? Specific events are less important than the general sense of things in your home.

Tom: I remember a few things. My mother did seem to take me to the doctor a lot, and it seemed that I missed a lot of school. And I remember that my mother seemed happiest and in her best mood when she was taking care of one of us. As for the money thing, my parents used to talk badly about people who lived in a certain neighborhood or who they saw drive by in fancy cars. I remember them saying things like, "They're nothing but a bunch of crooks!" My father used to talk very badly about his boss, and I remember once when we were coming home after a company picnic, my father ranted about how his boss was getting rich off his back.

Dr. G: In some respects, this automatic brain of yours is your new overprotective parent. It means well, but its response is a bit over the top. It is trying to protect you from all sorts of dangers. One way to look at it is if this overprotective parent had you wear a raincoat to school every day because of the possibility it might rain. Sometimes she might be right, but most of the time she would not. Similarly, the automatic brain always tries to prepare you for the worst-case scenario. Sometimes it might be right, but believing it, trusting it, and taking direction from it all the time, leads you to a state of constant "overprotection" and fear. As you can see, it is very draining.

———————

Francine is a 71-year-old retired and widowed grandmother, starting a new business.

Francine: Dr. G, lately I have been snapping at everyone. I just seem to boil inside over the stupidest things. I'm very anxious and stressed. The fact that I feel like I have no control makes things worse. It's all depressing me.

Dr. G: I can see how that would be upsetting. Have you ever had a problem like this?

Francine: Not really—in fact, quite the opposite. I usually don't speak up very much and have been fairly passive throughout my life. Now that I have decided to start my own business, I am very excited—probably more excited than I have ever been in my life. But the way I am reacting to things just doesn't make sense to me and honestly, it is making me physically ill.

Dr. G: Although this won't sit well with mental-health practitioners who think I am simplifying things too much, I find that the breeding ground of depression lies in the flight responsive of the automatic brain. If your AB detects danger, threat, or vulnerability it leads you to fight or flight. The latter often reveals itself as depression or withdrawal. Often when you feel as though you have no control this signals vulnerability, hence triggering your AB, and leading to the flight. Similarly, when your AB causes you to obsessively cling to the past, it is a tip off that that it senses your present situation as dangerous. Therefore, the sadness and depression that results helps you flee the danger. Depression becomes the cause and effect of you not fulfilling your dreams. It is the vehicle that helps you flee, or avoid the challenge (the "grave danger") and with this avoidance further depression results. This is why the direction of the automatic brain is not to be trusted. You can never win as it forms an endless loop of fight or flight.

Right now, the fight-or-flight reaction is being triggered in you, as your brain perceives danger in starting a new business. You don't want it to protect you, you don't need it to protect you, but it does—automatically. This is how you wind up with a feeling of not being in control—your brain is doing something automatically that seems counterproductive, yet you can't stop it. The perceived danger causes you either to act passively to flee, or to strike out aggressively to fight it. When there is anger or rage, or depression or withdrawal there is always a danger trigger lurking. Although you are far from childhood, I suspect that somewhere in the development of your brain some danger memories were established that became more than just the usual independence triggers.

Francine: As a child, I was never allowed to express anger. Do you think that has anything to do with it?

Dr. G: Absolutely. Can you say more about that?

Francine: Anytime he wanted to punish me, my father would go for weeks without speaking to me. I also got the message that I was lucky to be alive because my mother was not supposed to risk her life by getting pregnant again after her first baby died at birth. I was made to feel guilty for having a life.

Dr. G: What an awesome burden you had to carry! For you to remember specifics like this indicates that these memories were reinforced on a daily basis and contributed to the culture of the household. It all helped to solidify the danger memories your automatic brain would turn to in the future to deal with present or future danger. It's kind of what is guiding your feelings, thoughts, and reactions now. Not expressing yourself became the familiar imprint within your automatic brain. Thus your AB would forever associate self-expression with an unfamiliar, hence dangerous place.

What do all these scenarios have in common? For Phyllis, Tom, and Francine to receive love in their childhoods, they had to meet certain conditions. If they did not meet those conditions, their parents could deny them love and affection. You see, your parents' automatic brains were also driven by the independence and familiarity triggers. In order to preserve familiar (comfort zone) patterns of behavior, thus keeping the household "safe", they needed to preserve the status quo—even if that status quo was painful to you and them. One way to instinctively, automatically do that is to precondition love.

Never doubt that conditional love can strongly influence patterns of thought into adulthood. Dr. James Prescott and others have found that withholding of maternal love and bonding frequently results in a child who fails to thrive. Primate studies have shown that if the bond between parent and offspring is disrupted, the infant can die. In short, the intimate connection between love and survival plays an integral role in the establishment of our automatic brains. A home in which love is given and later withdrawn becomes a fertile ground for the formation of danger memories, and they can trigger the fight-or-flight response throughout our lives.

In Phyllis's case, in order to gain her mother's love she dared not look better than her mother. Her automatic brain goes into action now, in her adult life, whenever she tries to look good. For her, looking attractive triggers a danger memory that's tied to the withholding of love from her mother. It does not matter that her mother is dead; the danger memory is locked in place from early childhood.

In Tom's case, in order to gain his mother's love, he needed to be sick. The automatic brain is triggered now in his adult life when he is healthy. Tom has far exceeded his parents' wealth. Even now, they make half-joking remarks to him about it. But his real danger memory was implanted by growing up in a household that associated wealth with something negative. In order for him to continue to receive his parents' love, he needed to echo them in trashing the wealthy, and certainly not aspire to wealth for himself. Now that he is, in fact, one of them, the danger memory gets continually triggered. Being different from his parents and not needing their help is tantamount—in his automatic brain, at least—to losing their love. In an exaggerated way (a predictable quality of the AB), it represents a threat to his survival.

Tom's example points out why, for me, it is no mistake that the children of affluent people tend to grow up more affluent. You might think that those children were afforded more privileges, and that explains the phenomenon. I think it's more likely that growing up in a household where affluence is viewed in a positive light means wealth will never form a danger memory.

Francine's parents forbade her to speak her mind. Expressing herself, in her mind, could risk losing their love and hence jeopardize her survival. The silent treatment reinforced the danger of voicing her opinion. The fight-or-flight response in her adult life is trying to keep her from danger—in other words, trying to shut her up. When the response kicks in, she could flee by passively doing nothing, withdraw, and become depressed, holding it in as she did for years. Or now, more recently, she has started to fight, acting aggressively, boiling over with anger or rage.

In the early 2008, we were all shocked by the scandal involving the former New York Governor Eliot Spitzer. From several articles, I learned a little about Spitzer's father and the relationship he had with his children. Journalists have written much about the elder Spitzer's personality and the pressure for excellence he imposed upon his children, especially the former governor. In order to retain his father's love, he felt he had to appear strong, although in his heart he may have felt weak. Young Eliot was physically very skinny, and may have felt he could never live up to his father's demands.

As with most danger memories, this type of conflict was strongly imprinted by the time Eliot Spitzer was a young teen. As he became successful, any situation that suggested he was weak would trigger his automatic brain, because weakness would place his father's love in danger. To protect himself from the ultimate threat to survival—loss of parental love—his mind continued to guide him down the "protective" pathway, demonstrating strength, not being wimpy. In my view, this ultimately led to behaviors that were mean-spirited (personal attacks on his foes) or aimed at proving his machismo (dominance over women). His behavior was driven by his automatic brain's attempt to protect him from danger. Being unaware of the automatic brain often leads to self-destructive behavior. That certainly seems to be the case with Eliot Spitzer.

A term often used in describing the former governor is "egotistical." My definition of ego is the part of our brain dedicated to the protection and survival of our physical body—i.e., the automatic brain. Our ego, or AB, influences our life when we believe, trust, and take direction from the physical symptoms and thoughts it generates in order to shore up our chances of survival. Ironically, though, what the ego does to help us survive can kill us. It is always running in the background, automatically, and will make sure that it controls our life. As you read this and think how it pertains to your life and childhood—and I hope you will do that—you must keep in mind that your parents, like most of us, probably weren't aware of their automatic brains. But they were certainly controlled by their automatic brain's influence of their behavior toward you.

Danger memories and how they affect your automatic brain could be at the center of your relationship problems today. For instance, what if your spouse is less interested in intimacy than you? Perhaps he or she experienced situations when he or she was younger where intimacy led to pain, sadness, or was abusive. Therefore, intimacy is a danger and will trigger the automatic brain leading your spouse to withdraw from it or fight it with anger or hostility. How does this affect your relationship? Quite simply, you being denied the love and intimacy from your spouse will trigger your AB causing you to have behaviors and thoughts that cause you to fight or flee (seen with anger or rage, denying your spouse affection, or an affair).

Understanding our AB doesn't necessarily require psychoanalysis. All we need is to realize that our unwanted behaviors and thoughts are driven by an automatic brain that's trying to protect us. That brain may very well be acting on erroneous, childish input. The key is to know what the input consists of, as in the above real examples. Once, you become aware of what is triggering you to react in a certain fashion, it becomes much easier to be in control of your life and your relationships instead of them controlling you.

CHAPTER EIGHT

A No Win Situation

❦

*"I'm afraid sometimes you'll play lonely games too,
games you can't win, because you'll play against you."*

–Dr. Seuss

Years ago, I heard a silly joke that goes something like this: On his birthday, a young boy went to visit his grandmother. She presented him with two sweaters – a red one and a blue one. The next week he went back to visit and proudly wore the blue one. His grandmother looked at him and replied, "What, the red one you didn't like?"

Always operating in the background in our daily lives is our automatic brain. The AB is what looks out to protect our physical body, ensuring its survival. It will employ any means possible to do its job. Its primary weapon is the physical response of stress—the fight-or-flight reaction driven by adrenaline and cortisol, and the emotional response of stress—the thoughts generated by the multitude of electrical and hormonal impulses. The AB runs 24/7. When it detects danger, wham! It goes into full battle mode.

As we have seen, the way our AB interprets danger is different for every individual, but the physical response is universal. The emotional response differs along with the differing thoughts our mind conjures up. These thoughts are often very strong and persuasive. The reality, however, is that the only purpose of our AB is to look out for our survival. Because of this responsibility, the automatic brain becomes the grandmother, and you can never win against this grandmother!

I work with many patients who want to make changes in their life, but constantly stumble as they take one-step forward, two steps back. This happens with both purely physical problems, like obesity, and emotional problems, like anxiety. The common complaint that these people share is that they do not feel in control. They repeatedly react automatically to the same danger situations. I help them identify the specific situations that represent danger and make them feel anxious and uncomfortable. The dangers they readily identify do not seem to arise from childhood danger memories, but rather relate to any situations that make them feel vulnerable. The dangers of the present almost always connect with danger memories formed during childhood, but one need not always explore these to make changes now.

Our automatic brain equates vulnerability with leaving us open to be destroyed. Seems a bit dramatic, but as I said before and will continually emphasize throughout this book, the AB tends to generalize and to exaggerate. Many people view the threat of embarrassment as putting themselves in a vulnerable position. Others have told me that when critiqued or criticized, their AB's fight-or-flight mechanism is triggered. Not surprisingly, criticism is interpreted by the AB as dangerous and making one vulnerable. Perhaps the greatest vulnerability stimulus of all is change, especially moving from a known to an unknown situation. All through our lives, with greater freedom and independence comes that fear of the unknown. The future itself is the great unknown and when our thoughts drift there, they become a trigger for the AB and all the fight or flight mechanics that follow.

I recall an interesting phenomenon from my first couple of years of practice. Any time I ran into a patient in the supermarket, mall, movies, or anywhere outside the office, I felt a twinge of discomfort. This acted as a trigger to my automatic brain. My AB was reacting to a sense of vulnerability. In some ways, I was now exposed as just an ordinary Joe and not the doctor behind a white coat. I was caught out in the open, so to speak, and open to being stomped on and crushed. Not really, of course, but as I say, the AB tends to exaggerate danger. If I had believed, trusted, or taken direction from my automatic brain at those moments, I might have avoided public places, just to play it safe.

So, let's say I had followed those thoughts and actually did avoid going out. Then avoiding going out would have presented another situation. Since the AB does not discriminate, I could expect that new thoughts would develop to "protect" me; perhaps a thought like, "You can't be successful as a doctor if you can't go out in public. What will your patients think?" A long time ago, I made a decision not to believe, trust, or take direction from my automatic brain; for if I did, I would be like the grandson forever trying to play to the grandmother who represents a no-win scenario. What I have learned, and what you will see in the next chapter, that doing the opposite of what the AB directs is more an accurate guide. Therefore, my mantra now is that "vulnerability is my greatest asset." Yes, that terrifying, subservient producing condition is actually something that can propel me further and put me in a safer more respected place.

Many of us go through the day content to follow the messages of our automatic brain. This can make us feel stuck and pigeonhole us into a very narrow definition of ourselves. When we follow the instructions of just one thought process, we provoke contrary thoughts that bring us back to where we started, making any kind of change difficult to achieve (as above: vulnerable to be seen outside the secure confines of the doctor's office, which evokes the following thought: "how could you be successful as a doctor, then?" Following this thought leads me to go out and about. Being out and about leads me to feeling vulnerable to be seen outside the secure confines of the doctor's office, evoking the thought: "how could you be successful…?" It keeps going round and round).

Many people maintain that very narrow automatic-brain definition of themselves to avoid the trigger of change. You may define yourself by your job, your family, your financial status, your health condition, the color of your hair, or perhaps by others' expectations of you. People look at my family and me and expect us to be and act in a certain way, because I am a doctor. So, when I decided to learn to play the drums a few years ago and play in a rock and roll band, I was venturing into uncharted waters. After all, I had never played drums as a kid.

Our band started practicing several months before our first public performance. The months leading up to this gig, I was feeling quite confident, never feeling too much in danger. A week before the performance, however, my automatic brain detected danger approaching. The thoughts that began to run through my brain were hopelessly wacky. My AB was trying desperately to protect me from the "danger" of performing. "Who do you think you are?" it seemed to say. "You can't play the drums. You're an amateur. You'll screw up!" The danger of criticism, embarrassment, change, freedom, you name it, I was laying myself out there and my automatic brain automatically was trying to reign me into safety. Since I knew enough not to believe or trust anything it told me, I did not take its direction, because I know if I had, I'd have had thoughts like, "You're weak! You can't face an audience! What are you, some kind of a wimp?" That would be the automatic brain trying to protect me from weakness. I was getting conflicting advice from my automatic brain—one side wanted to keep me from the danger of failure as a performer, and the other side didn't want me to look like a loser by giving up. So—what the hell, I figured—I went out there and performed. You see, "vulnerability is my greatest asset." From what I was told, we sounded pretty good then and I since have secured myself as a key element of our band as we continue to play publically.

Recently I met with Mark, a successful 52- year-old executive and father of three. Mark has been obese for all of his adult life, and recently another physician diagnosed him with diabetes.

Mark hates being controlled by people critiquing or criticizing him. I told him his excessive eating and being unfit must be somehow comforting. His automatic brain was associating sensible eating and being fit with danger. His AB was working around the clock to protect him from the "danger" of having a fit body and eating sensibly, and steering him into a comfort zone. He admitted that eating sensibly made him feel controlled. He felt that in social situations people would evaluate what he was eating and critique him on it. He worried that if he ate healthy foods, people might think he was a vegan nut or some other kind of weirdo. He felt that in his professional and personal life, he was controlled by too many rules, and when he went out to eat, he wanted no rules, no control.

Mark's automatic brain interprets eating sensibly and fitness as dangerous, and making him vulnerable. He feels comfort when he eats without restrictions or rules, and with no one telling him what to do. He feels free, less stressed. Unfortunately, that is not where he wants to be. He came to me because he wanted to change. He wants to get fit, eat sensibly, and not have diabetes. But he's stuck in a false comfort zone.

The greatest irony of the automatic brain is that it tricks us into thinking that we are making decisions that help us. I pointed out to Mark that the thing his brain wants him to flee—being controlled— is exactly what his automatic brain is imposing on him. His AB controls him, driving him into a box. As I will show later, it is his mind that wants to escape that box, but he puts full faith in his automatic brain that associates the box with comfort and safety, repeatedly leading him to fight or flee anytime he tries to leave. The fight is the anger he feels when others criticize him; the flight becomes the self-medicating behavior (food being the medication) he feels by eating without control. Far from being crazy, this kind of dilemma is more the norm than the exception.

Why do many people hate public speaking? Standing up in front of a crowd leaves you open to attack, or at least public humiliation. What if your pants fall down, or you have some mucus come out of your nose when you sneeze, or your zipper is down throughout the presentation and you have no clue? Whether conscious or not, the AB generates these type of lurking fears to urge you to fight or flee such exposure. To play it safe, most people avoid the risk—that is, they flee the danger, though inside, they wish they had the courage to do it.

Our automatic brain constantly tries to drive us into safety. Anything unfamiliar triggers the specter of a lurking saber-tooth tiger. For some, the familiar is being sick and miserable. This defines them; it becomes who they are. Changing—becoming healthy— would put them in an unfamiliar environment, and their AB determines that to be dangerous.

Throughout my career I have known patients who stay in hurtful relationships. Why? Because that is what they know; it is familiar to them. Their automatic brain is trying to protect them from uncharted waters. It's fear of the unknown, a powerful trigger of the automatic brain that seeks to protect us from potential danger. The state of misery and sickness is actually comforting and makes us feel less vulnerable, because we know what to expect. Even in this comfort zone of misery, the AB tries to protect us and move us out, but as we take the one-step-forward by trying to leave the misery, the need for the familiar kicks in again to bounce us right back. This ping-pong nature of the automatic brain drives much of human behavior and makes up much of human nature.

Take Diane for example. For Diane, money, or the lack of it, is a continual trigger of the automatic brain and a regular cause of stress. Over the past two years, our discussions have seemed always to turn to her financial hardships. I'm a doctor, not a financial planner, so she wasn't coming to me primarily for financial advice. But it was apparent that her concern about money was affecting her health, so I asked her, "If you won the lottery today, would that solve your problems?" She thought for a moment, and said, "Yes, I believe it would." I then proposed the following scenario, "Ok, great, you just won the lottery. You are sitting in your beach chair on a fine, white Hawaiian beach. Above you, a thatched bamboo umbrella shields you from the hot sun blazing in the cloudless noonday sky. A gentle breeze caresses your face, as you watch dolphins playfully jumping in and out of the translucent aqua water. Moving the cocktail umbrella to the side, you take a sip of the smoothest pina colada you have ever had. Wow—it feels so good, doesn't it?"

"But then," I continue, "what do you feel? A twinge of pain in your chest? A slight pant, feeling you can't take a deep breath? You wonder, 'Am I having a heart attack? What about the pain in my leg? Could it be cancer?' The fight-or-flight thoughts keep coming. 'Oh my Lord, I'm scared.'"

Let me explain. For Diane, the lack of money represented danger, and her automatic brain forever played in the background, continually generating thoughts about this danger—obsessively thinking about her bills, how she would pay them, what if she lost her job—always trying to prepare her to appropriately fight or flee this danger. The hypothetical lottery winnings seemed to be the solution to this danger. What she found though, in this example, is that once she could be in a supposedly safe place—the place where her automatic brain seemed to want her—she would find that her AB was still on alert, because that is what it does, relentlessly trying to protect her from danger that might be lurking even in this safe place. Diane agreed that this is likely where her brain would go. She now understands the no-win dynamic of her automatic brain, the same dynamic that applies to all of our automatic brains.

Marjorie is a 74-year-old woman with a long history of high blood pressure. Recently, we have succeeded in lowering her blood pressure medication due to excellent control. During one of her recent visits, she expressed concern that her blood pressure is now low; something must be wrong. High blood pressure represented a danger to her automatic brain and now normal blood pressure triggers a sense that something must now be wrong. Hence, when we listen to our automatic brains, our "protector," we live in a constant state of warning.

I know not to believe, trust, or take direction from my automatic brain. I recall that when I was well into training for my first marathon, when I had run about three miles and was starting to feel a little tired, I would get a thought, "I'll never make 26.2 miles if I'm a little tired after only three. I had better stop or slow down because I might have a heart attack (straight from my danger memory)." However, if I did not maintain a certain running pace, I'd get thoughts like, "You're running too slow, pick it up," (That stemmed from my brain's feeling of being vulnerable to being outperformed by someone else.) I have spoken with many runners and they share with me the same conflicting tapes playing in their head.

As our ABs try to use reality to protect us, the most real thing is the prospect that when the limits of a comfort zone are broken down—even the "comfort" of sickness or misery—our automatic brain will continue to fire. It creates thoughts like, "Whoa, what am I doing here?" It will then go on a frenzied search of reasons to drag us back, to flee or violently fight, the new "danger."

Stan is frustrated with his life. At 46, he has suffered from back pain for many years, pain so severe, he tells me, that it prevents him from going out and meeting new people. Stan was not happy with his life, and said that he really wanted a social life. Yet every time he ventured out, the reality of the back pain would pull him back. "How can I do these things if

I'm in pain?" he wondered. We concluded that the pain was actually protecting him from the danger of meeting new people. If he were able to go out and establish new relationships those relationships could fail; indeed, that was the pattern for the better part of his 46 years. In other words, as Stan listens to his automatic brain he is forced to conclude, "I'm damned if I do, damned if I don't."

Even though my AB fires up when it perceives vulnerability, I have learned, as I wrote before, that vulnerability is one of my greatest assets. When I share my personal thoughts with you, my readers, a world of respect opens up. And my messages, I hope, allow others to see that their vulnerability can serve them well and not only aid in their survival, but help them thrive. If I were fully to believe, trust, and take direction from my AB, I would not be writing this book, as I am exposing myself, not just to a relatively small number of people in my personal and professional circle, but also to the world!

Next, I will explain how we can begin changing the trust we have in our AB. Sounds daunting, perhaps, however it is easier than one might think. Believing and trusting the possibility of change is the first step in creating the sustainable happy, healthy, and fulfilled life that we need, want, and deserve.

CHAPTER NINE

The Ultimate Challenge

❧❧❧

"Anyone can make things bigger and more complex . . . It takes a touch of genius—and a lot of courage—to move in the opposite direction."

–John Dryden

To provide further insight into the above definition of genius, let me enlist the insight of two of the most profound and influential thinkers of our time: Larry David and Jerry Seinfeld. In the following conversation from an episode of Seinfeld, you will see the power of not listening to the automatic brain.

The scene opens with George gazing out over what appears to be a beach. Next, cut to George arriving at Monk's Diner and sitting at a booth with Jerry and Elaine.

Jerry (looking up as George enters): Speaking of having it all…Where were you?

George: I went to the beach.

Jerry and Elaine (looking at each other, smiling): Ahh, the beach.

George (as he sits down): It's not working Jerry. It's just not working.

Jerry: What is it that isn't working?

George: Why did it all turn out like this for me? I had so much promise. I was personable, I was bright…maybe not academically speaking…It all came very clear to me sitting out there today—every single decision I've made in my entire life has been wrong. My life is the complete opposite of everything I wanted to be. Every instinct I have, in every aspect of life, be it something to wear, something to eat, it's all been wrong. Every one.

The waitress approaches the booth.

Waitress (to George): Tuna on toast, coleslaw, cup of coffee?

George: Yeah.

The waitress begins to walk away.

George: No, no, no, wait a minute. (The waitress comes back.) I always have tuna on toast. Nothing's ever worked out for me with tuna on toast. I want the complete opposite: Chicken salad, on rye, untoasted ... and a cup of tea.

Elaine: Well, there's no telling what can happen from this.

Jerry: You know chicken salad is not the opposite of tuna, salmon is the opposite of tuna, 'cause salmon swim against the current, and the tuna swim with it.

George: Good for the tuna. (A blonde, sitting at the counter across from the group, looks at George.)

Elaine: Ah, George, you know, that woman just looked at you.

George: So what? What am I supposed to do?

Elaine: Go talk to her.

George: Elaine, bald men, with no jobs, and no money, who live with their parents, don't approach strange women.

Jerry: Well here's your chance to try the opposite. Instead of tuna salad and being intimidated by women, chicken salad and going right up to them.

George: Yeah, I should do the opposite, I should.

Jerry: If every instinct you have is wrong, then the opposite would have to be right.

George: Yes, I will do the opposite. I used to sit here and do nothing, and regret it for the rest of the day, so now I will do the opposite, and I will do something! (He goes over to the woman.)

George: Excuse me, I couldn't help but notice that you were looking in my direction.

Woman: Oh yes, I was. You just ordered the same exact lunch as me.

George (he takes a deep breath): My name is George. I'm unemployed and I live with my parents.

Woman (extending her hand and leaning toward George): I'm Victoria. Hi.

———————————

For years, George listened to the edicts of his automatic brain. This day he decides not to listen to it, to break from its inexorable grip. In order to do that, he needs to take a contrarian approach. His AB looks for evidence to protect him from slaughter—bald man, no job, no money, living at home—and I guess it didn't have to look very far! Instead of believing, trusting, and taking direction from the impulse, he decides to go the other way—and do the opposite of what his AB suggests. And lo and behold, not only does George "get the girl," but her uncle works for the

NY Yankees. In another classic scene, George lands the job as assistant to the traveling secretary by telling George Steinbrenner how he has totally mismanaged the Yankee organization for 20 years!

As we saw in the last chapter, taking direction from our automatic brain bounces us back and forth without permitting us to grow in the direction we want. To understand how to get the upper hand from the AB, it is important to become aware of when it fires. For most of us, our automatic brain drives us throughout our lives, until we reach an epiphany of sorts—as George does when he decides to go after the girl—when the choice of fight or flight becomes unbearable. George does not consciously identify any of his triggers, nor is he aware of any specific danger memory. Instead, he only recognizes that something always sabotages him and keeps him from getting where he wants to go, from being who he wants to be. The saboteur, of course, is his automatic brain. But instead of letting the details drag him down, this time he decides simply to do the opposite of usual.

For a very, very long time the automatic brain has been crucial to our survival. For a survival mechanism to be successful, it should not involve complicated choices and decision-making. That's how it works with the automatic brain—the decision comes down to fighting or fleeing in the face of perceived danger. That was our mental roadmap way back when, and it's still our mental roadmap in the 21st Century. Even today, when we perceive danger, our automatic brain directs us to fight or flee. This decision became the defining feature of our AB. Fight-or-flight thoughts have become a major part of our daily decision-making, but rarely are they in response to real danger. So automatic are they that that we classify them as instinct.

Attempting to meddle with instinct seems wrong, right? But what if following our instinct and automatic impulses has taken us down a path towards confusion? Is it still wrong?

Before we can achieve our true potential, we must end our total reliance on our protective automatic brain. "But if I do that," you may reply, "how will I know when real danger is approaching? I could be leaving myself open to being hurt or maybe even killed!" The fact is by not believing, trusting, or taking direction from this "instinct," you will be better prepared to recognize true danger; your mind will not be clouded by the perpetual circuit of electrical impulses and hormones the generated by the AB. You will be more clear and able. Solutions will pop into your head, effortlessly. The physical response, if needed, will be there. Just like Professor John Nash's delusions, it is always with you ready for you to flip the switch. (After all, it's been with us for some 200,000+ years.) But your mind will decide when to flip the switch, not the circuitous thoughts generated by the AB.

Now, I know that you probably consider yourself a good person. You could not possibly be one of those people who are driven solely by the automatic brain and its incessant need to make you stand above others—those are other people. Even rich people got rich—didn't they?—by being insensitive to others. But that's not you—you could not be like Donald Trump, because you could not tell someone, "You're fired!" Well, I hate to disillusion you, but the reality is that your automatic brain is the same as the Donald's! What may set you apart, though, is that you decide to believe, trust, and take direction from them in a different way.

While kayaking on vacation, as part of an ecology tour, we traveled through canals and some open water en route to a nature preserve. Including our guide in his single, the group occupied three double-seated kayaks, including my wife's and mine. There was no rush, but occasionally I would find myself thinking, "Paddle harder, they're catching up." This was my automatic brain reacting to the possible danger of being "one-upped". Being one-upped is associated with being snuffed out (oh, that overly dramatic automatic brain of ours).

As I became aware of what was happening, I decided not to take direction from my AB. The choice I made was to enjoy the beautiful, tranquil waters, the wonderful experience with my wife, and the extraordinary physical exercise. I decided to paddle motivated only by these factors. And my experience was richer for rejecting the fight direction—the aggressive demands—of my automatic brain. (Physical exertion and athletic competition, incidentally, are superb ways to sublimate the power of the automatic brain; more on that subject later).

Whether our fight or flight is aggressive or passive, respectively, we still fall victim to it mostly below our level of awareness. Most of his life, George adopted a passive response to his relationships with women. But in the episode I've described, he proceeds in the direction directly opposite from the one his AB directs. His automatic brain would steer him towards passivity, but he bucks it, and chooses assertion.

The automatic brain, guided by its fight-or-flight response, can show up in the most unexpected of circumstances. In casual conversations with friends, aggressive behavior masks itself as "one-upmanship." The individuals involved are not aware of what drives them. Are people bad when they brag to us that their little Joey is walking at 8 months old, knowing that your child is still holding on for dear life at 14 months? Competing against another is an automatic drive, a reflex, essentially an evolutionary programming of the AB to ensure the survival of the physical body. But aggression even at these levels never results in satisfaction; instead, it has us always trying to position ourselves above others and there always seems to be one more above us. The irony is, however, that in situations when the automatic brain tries to help us survive, we truly do not need it.

Rejecting our instinct is a monumental challenge, and such change brings about a flurry of fight-or-flight thoughts, not to mention the physical signs that go along with it. Tossing out the dominance of our AB puts us on the path to the ultimate uncharted destination. Unfortunately, when we venture upon uncharted waters, we often succumb to the powerful urge of our automatic brain to flee. The feeling of, "Oh my God, how did I get here, what have I done?" may set in. This is not surprising, and is the signal to adopt a contrarian approach. How do I know? Because, if the circumstances in which we exist are wrong, then adopting the opposite circumstances must be right (thank you, Jerry Seinfeld).

As I snorkeled while on vacation, I had fleeting thoughts that I would suddenly come face to face with a shark (even though sharks have never been sighted in this area). Responding to this situation, I could have fled it and gotten out of the water, or fought it, demanding that the resort take precautions to assure the safety of their guests and refusing to go back in the water until they did. I elected to do the opposite of my AB's dictates, I continued to snorkel. Wonder of wonders, I lived to tell about it (what a risk taker I am!).

During Olympic day at my daughters' elementary school, as my 9-year old daughter stood, in 85 degree and 90 percent humidity, at the starting line for the 400-meter race, I had a crazy fleeting image of her collapsing at the finish line with a seizure, heat stroke if you will. I could have responded passively by removing her from the danger and thus fleeing my danger, or I could have acted aggressively by demanding that the entire race be called off and reprimanding the principal and teachers for their lack of common sense in holding a race in that kind of heat. I chose the opposite of my automatic brain's direction, and sat back and enjoyed my daughter's determination.

Knowing when to respond in a manner opposite from the direction your AB is pushing you takes some practice. It helps if you can recognize signs that the automatic brain is working to protect you from perceived

danger. Some of the physical symptoms, caused by the release of adrenaline and cortisol, include rapid heartbeat and trembling (see Chapter 2).
When you feel these physical sensations, you can be pretty sure that your
automatic brain is working (falsely) to protect you—unless, of course, it's
responding to a real danger. Another dead giveaway are fleeting thoughts.
Whenever you feel relaxed, happy, peaceful, enjoying the moment and a
fleeting thought pops into your head about something that is disturbing
(as my thoughts above) you can be assured that your automatic brain has
generated them for the purpose of removing you from or making you fight
these "dangerous" conditions.

If you notice yourself having the symptoms of a protective AB, you
can assume that your automatic brain is on a wild data search of your
memory banks trying to match up present circumstance with stored danger memories. George's danger memories dealt mostly with his physical
appearance. What held him back every time was his awareness of being
bald and short. Short stature makes someone more physically vulnerable
(at least to the automatic brain) and hence jeopardizes survival (oh, so
dramatic is the AB!). Therefore, as with George, his height automatically
triggered a passive (flight) response throughout his life. He needed to
avoid any situation where that feature would place him in a vulnerable
position. (Others might adopt a more aggressive fight response, such as
the well known Napoleon complex).

A common trigger deals with relationship issues. I will go out on a
limb and state that one particular trigger is genetically lodged within our
danger memories: monogamy. Here's what I mean: The purpose of our
automatic brain is the survival of our physical body. To assure that our
physical body lives on is to assure that our DNA (part of our physical existence) will survive and be passed on (shoring up our immortality). A
monogamous relationship—i.e., restricting ourselves to one sexual part-

ner—puts this hereditary survival in jeopardy, at least as processed by the AB. If you're not aware of this inner connection, monogamy may be difficult to maintain. The automatic brain constantly attempts to push you away from it, producing a persistent fight-or-flight conflict. This conflict, you may not be surprised to learn, is especially noticeable as we approach the end of our reproductive life—the so-called mid-life crisis. If the strong drive for DNA survival becomes a threat to our happiness and relationship stability, it's clear that we need to move in the opposite direction by doing whatever is necessary to protect our own monogamy. How does the automatic brain reveal itself in response to the monogamy danger? Through fight or flight, of course. The fight may be represented by aggressive behavior such as verbal abuse, constant arguing, or constantly comparing your spouse with someone else. The flight might be represented by an affair. I choose this example to illustrate the insidious nature of our automatic brain, and how important it may be to move in a direction opposite from its commands.

Whenever I have a public speaking engagement, as my name is being announced I feel my heart rate quicken. This is one of the signs that my AB is alerting me to run the other way, away from danger. I have learned to recognize this, and I make the decision to move in the opposite direction and continue on with the speaking engagement.

Is opposing the draining force of the AB the ultimate challenge? Perhaps. Recognizing what the automatic brain wants us to do is certainly a good way to decide which direction we would be better off moving—that is, in the opposite direction.

Making changes always triggers the automatic brain. Leaving our familiar home, even if that home is preventing us from growing, leads to a flurry of activity designed to keep us there in safety, out of harm's way. Recognizing that much of our instinctive behavior is in reality the workings of our AB is the first step to breaking the cycle we saw in the previous chapter. To grow, you often have to move in the direction opposite the one set by your automatic brain's agenda. To accomplish this contrarian strategy, we must zero in on the core of our automatic brain—our thoughts. Next, I will describe a simple exercise to help accomplish this and to begin breaking down the barriers that interfere with our quest for what we truly desire in our lives.

CHAPTER TEN

True Desires

"Just what you want to be, you will be in the end."

–Justin Hayward (Moody Blues)

Ever since I began sharing my book installments, people have been coming to me with issues that they feel I can address from my unique perspective. In this chapter, I will illustrate a technique I use to help myself and others move in a direction opposite the driving force of their automatic brains.

Recently, Mitch came to my office. Mitch is a high-level executive for a large retail merchandiser. Earlier this year, another company approached him with an offer to become an officer in their company. A problem that had been afflicting Mitch for several years seemed to be getting worse, especially after the offer. The problem: Mitch's fear of public speaking. During scheduled presentations, he had no problem. The PowerPoint slides or other props helped him effortlessly flow through his presentations. But anytime he had to give an impromptu presentation, whether a one-on-one business discussion or a speech in front of a large group, Mitch experienced a very strong urge to escape.

His automatic brain was interpreting these events as dangerous, and his two choices were (you guessed it) fight or flight. Physically, he went through classic panic symptoms—a racing pulse, sweaty forehead, and faster breathing. He feared that his throat would close up and he wouldn't be able to get the words out. Obviously, those are not good things for an executive to go through.

What I found significant was that this panic reaction had recently increased in frequency, duration, and severity. Mitch's response indicated that there had to be a danger lurking close by. As we spoke, it became clear that the special danger was the possibility of Mitch taking the new job. That prospect was setting his automatic brain in action. And once the AB goes to work, it is very persuasive, very draining. My goal was not necessarily to stop the AB, but to shift him to a purer, more rational decision-making process; to stop the incessant drain.

The Glassman Revelation Grid is a tool I use to help people compartmentalize certain thoughts and feelings to understand what is driving them. I use Revelation in the name because when completed, the grid reveals what they need to see. It looks like this:

Circumstance/Trigger	Danger	Comfort/Safety
	Box #1	Box #2
	Box #3	Box #4

For Mitch, we identified his trigger as the possibility of the new job, not actual public speaking. (The public speaking represented the plethora of danger memories in his automatic brain's data banks, which the AB picked up while on its wild data search to protect him). I asked him to think about what would be dangerous about his not taking the job; that is, staying where he was, not changing. This is important, because our automatic brain tries to drive us away from danger to safety. If we are not in a place we want to be, it is probably because we're listening to the automatic brain.

We started to fill in his grid, and it looked like this:

Circumstance/Trigger	Danger	Comfort/Safety
Not taking the job	Loss of professional stature; not realizing full financial potential; letting down colleagues (from new company who believe in me).	
Taking the job		

The next step was identifying what danger taking the job would represent:

Circumstance/Trigger	Danger	Comfort/Safety
Not taking the job		
Taking the job	Humiliation, embarrassment, vulnerability (because of panic when speaking "off the cuff"), lack of performance, loss of professional stature by failing to perform (i.e., I will mess up when trying to speak and not get respect).	

The next step was to determine what comfort and safety his automatic brain had determined he'd get from not taking the job:

Circumstance/Trigger	Danger	Comfort/Safety
Not taking the job		
Taking the job		Professionally most rewarding; the new company is so ripe for development that I can have a significant, positive impact on the company and entire industry; work with a dynamic, exciting team; realizing full financial potential; being in a place that I have often dreamed about.

Feeling a little like Monte Hall (the host of the popular '60s and '70s game show *Let's Make a Deal*), I asked Mitch behind which door (box) he would like to park himself if he had the choice. He responded, Box #4. In fact, if it were totally up to his free will, Mitch would park himself not only *behind* door #4, but also smack dab *in* it!

Regrettably, like Mitch, most of us don't act purely from free will when we make decisions. The automatic brain drives us, and even though it appears to be working in our best interest, it is operating from a primitive notion of survival and conjuring up for us all sorts of exaggerated, worst-case scenarios, using inaccurate data from danger memories. Even if a danger memory appears real and concrete (for instance, Mitch's throat actually did close and he was not able to speak), past experience does not necessarily predict future results. (You know—the same disclaimers you see on any mutual fund prospectus. In this case, at least, Wall Street is on the money!). However, your automatic brain will have you believe that all danger memories are carved in stone and will happen again. And all because it just wants you to survive; it is your overprotective parent.

So, let's look at Mitch's completed Revelation Grid:

Circumstance/Trigger	Danger	Comfort/Safety
Not taking the job	*Loss of professional stature; not realizing full financial potential; letting down colleagues (from new company who believe in me).*	Staying put; familiar, predictable job, therefore easier; avoiding the nervousness of changing; don't have to put myself out there and expose my disability of speaking impromptu; ability to retire soon with a pension; get out of the corporate rat race.
Taking the job	Humiliation, embarrassment, vulnerability (because of panic when speaking "off the cuff"), lack of performance, loss of professional stature by failing to perform (i.e., I will mess up when trying to speak and not get the respect).	*Professionally most rewarding; the new company is so ripe for development that I can have a significant, positive impact on the company and entire industry; work with a dynamic, exciting team; realizing full financial potential; being in a place that I have often dreamed about.*

For Mitch, as with most of us, the direction our automatic brain takes us is the self-sabotaging direction from bottom left (box #3) to top right (box #2). This is the direction of our AB and these boxes represent its rationale. The evidence is persuasive, strong, and draining; so are the physical symptoms that it generates. The challenge I proposed to Mitch was not to get rid of the AB dynamic, but to cultivate his thoughts so he could override the autopilot nature of his automatic brain and be able to move in the opposite direction. If he were to continue to follow its edicts, he would continuously bounce between Box #2 and Box #3. Getting him to where he wants to be meant, in short, that his direction of thought had to move him from top left to bottom right.

The AB relies on future possibilities and past failures. It prepares us for the worst-case scenario. The power of free will—the power of our mind—resides in the present. To help Mitch move to his desired goal, I showed him some techniques for keeping focused on the tasks of the moment. For example, I made him aware that the immediate fight-or-flight physical response, the adrenaline surge, lasts only about a minute unless fight-or-flight thinking fuels it with future possibilities. Since the physical response can be powerful, the first step is to breathe in slowly through the nose and out through the mouth (I will discuss breathing techniques in detail in future chapters). This can be done quietly and discretely in front of people, without their awareness.

At the same time, I explained that it is important to generate a specific mantra or affirmation within him, dealing with the immediate danger. For Mitch, the physical sensation itself is very scary. Once the fear is over, he feels better, but often the damage is done—in other words, he already feels that he embarrassed himself with cracking voice or no voice or actually having to excuse himself from the room.

Since adrenaline is a stimulant, it causes us to act more quickly and erratically—to breathe faster, move faster, and if engaged in conversation or debate, to talk faster. All of this adds up to the possibility of increased danger of messing up. I suggested that when he feels the adrenaline beginning to surge, he could affirm something like, "The adrenaline is telling me to act…to act deliberately, slowly, and assertively." The thought of screwing up and exposing himself as inadequate, thus preventing him from succeeding, can be countered with a second mantra: "Today I'm going to expose myself…I'm exposing myself as strong, powerful, and influential."

Acknowledging the fear and transforming it into something empowering is an effective strategy for aborting the paralysis of the automatic brain. By this technique, Mitch is acknowledging his automatic brain and using his more advanced mind to override it. Since the automatic brain will always be around, even when someone is in Box #4, it will fire. However, when residing in a desired place, it becomes easier and easier not to believe, trust, or take direction from it. I will expand on this in later chapters.

Mitch successfully utilized these techniques. Feeling substantially empowered with the knowledge of the automatic brain, he landed the job of his dreams—a job that resulted in a high six figure income with the prospect for continued personally and professional growth.

My decision to write this book fired up my own automatic brain. My Glassman Revelation Grid looks like this:

Circumstance/Trigger	Danger	Comfort/Safety
Not writing book	*Not realizing true potential; not being a good example for my kids (i.e., having an idea but not pursing it or persevering).*	Staying in a familiar place—being a small-town doctor; not delving into deeper thoughts; not exposing personal insights to a large audience; I'm already respected locally, not open to wider critiques.
Writing book	Exposing myself by sharing personal examples; vulnerable, showing weakness; somebody will steal my ideas and call it their own before a publisher picks it up; colleagues and others who don't accept my theories will talk negatively about me perhaps ridicule me; friends and family may feel skittish about hanging around me as they may think I am analyzing their behavior or think of me as a little weird; becoming famous, jeopardizing humility; money rewards that will make others uncomfortable to be around me; I may fail to get it published as with other attempts in the past; paying for editing of a book that may never be published and earn back the investment; if I do become famous people will learn that I didn't go to Harvard or Yale; Nobody will buy it.	*Sharing my viewpoints, which I feel can help many people; creating something I have always dreamed of doing; financial reward; proving that I can make manifest something that started with a simple idea; coalescing and organizing my thoughts to help me understand myself. Sharing with the world ideas that I feel are unique and life affirming; ideas that could improve the lives of many*

Contained within my grid is the goal for writing this book. It is a quest to help me and you come face to face with our pure potential: to discover the power of our mind. As we move on from understanding our automatic brain, I will guide you, in the second part of this book, towards finding the power of your mind—our true potential, our connection with the universe, our connection to our inner guidance, to the divinity that exists within each of us. The context of life experience must frame this pursuit. Behind door (box) #4 is where our mind is hiding. In order to find it, we must first learn to live with our automatic brain around, even enjoy it, but never allow it to rule us. We want to learn how to control our AB, not have it control us. For when we do, it remains a formidable block in discovering the power of our mind, and it drains us of our life's purpose.

Here are some more real-life examples of individuals using the Revelation Grid to help them understand the workings of their AB. Remember Phyllis in Chapter 7, whose mother thought she was selfish for looking good? Her grid is on the next page:

Circumstance/Trigger	Danger	Comfort/Safety
Eating without control (unfit body)	*Becoming a fat old lady; difficulty breathing; low self-esteem; less physically fit; future illness, especially diabetes; lack of control.*	Like the way food makes me feel; don't have to listen to anyone; can eat as I like, no stress or restriction; no thinking while enjoying social events.
Eating with control (fit body)	Caring only about myself; being a showoff; more stress/pressure from having to be always in control; constantly thinking about food; becoming a new obsession.	*More energy; enhanced sexual relationship with husband; able to run, jump, and play with children; higher self-esteem; less difficulty fitting into clothing; more comfortable with my body; feeling more principled, like I am doing the right thing; better quality of life; more patience.*

Like most people who complete this grid, when asked which box she wanted to move toward, Phyllis said box #4. She noticed her automatic brain firing every time she tried to control her eating. It wasn't always obvious, but her efforts to eat more responsibly were continually sabotaged by thoughts about the danger her AB associated with controlling eating. I suggested several mantras: "I am selfish...selfish because I know that when I take care of myself I can best take care of others." "I am a showoff...I am showing off my ability to create the person I dream about." When she finds herself in a potentially sabotaging situation as at an all-you-can-eat buffet, she could use the mantra: "Short term gain, long term pain."

Bernice is a 40-year-old mother of three. She came to me because of several issues; the most significant, she felt, was her anger. Since childhood, she had viewed herself as a person who would serve to keep the peace. She felt that she could handle most situations without anger. But about a year ago, she discovered that her business partner was cheating her and the small business that bore both of their names. Money coming into the business was usually in the form of checks, some made out to both of them, others made out to just one of them. What Bernice learned was that her partner was taking the checks made out only to her partner (not bearing Bernice's name) and depositing them in her personal checking account. Additionally, she found that even checks with her name on them were deposited in a phantom business account of which Bernice had no knowledge.

The fact that her partner, years before, had committed similar indiscretions, intensified Bernice's anger. At that time, they had reconciled for the good of the business. This time they terminated their relationship. But Bernice was unable to get rid of her anger, which was making her physically sick and standing in the way of her moving forward.

We came up with the following Revelation Grid:

Circumstance/Trigger	Danger	Comfort/Safety
Anger	*Makes me short-tempered with everyone; no patience with anyone; hurts me—doesn't feel like me; takes my energy away, draining; don't like it, physically tiring; guard is always up; affects my trust in everyone and everything; nothing bad in relationships surprises me anymore.*	Serves as a constant reminder of what happened so I don't let it happen again—avoid being blind-sided; ongoing punishment of the person who hurt me even though she wants to reconcile again; easier to give into the anger than to think about how to let it go.
Releasing anger (letting go)	Guard is down, opening me up to getting taken advantage of again; need to start a new business on my own; appear weak; let my former partner off the hook.	*Relieve mental pressure—freedom; higher level of functioning; able to think more clearly as I approach new business with personal confidence; able to go it on my own without using another person as a crutch; less crying; operating on a higher level*

As Bernice recognized, taking direction from our AB is the easy way to go. Since it fires automatically, following it is the path of least resistance, it is our default response. But the path of the AB leads us away from where we wish to be. Despite everything, Bernice desires to reside behind door #4. Right now, she is bouncing between #2 and #3. How does she get to where she wants to be, *before* the end (as Justin Hayward says)? How does she find out what life is like behind door #4? She accomplishes this by looking at the grid and completely rejecting every thought in box 2 and 3. By living in box #4 she effectively eliminates any possibility of danger and increases the likelihood of safety far more than by following what's in boxes #2 and #3. She believes 100 percent in box 4—not 25 percent, or 50 percent, or 75 percent, or 99.99 percent, but 100 percent believe. When she believes in even an iota of what her AB has generated, it opens the floodgates. Picture this. On one side is an ocean of turbulent water. On the other side, is a beautiful pasture, with blooming tranquil gardens. Separating these two areas is a dike, a dam. There you are with your finger in the dike. The pastures represent your mind and the turbulent waters are the constant activity of your automatic brain. When you release your finger and allow the trickle of water to seep in, representing a smidgeon of belief in those waters, what you find is that the trickle eventually becomes a steady flow and the hole gets bigger, and bigger, and bigger, and bigger. Eventually, the garden floods and your mind is drowning in a state of overwhelm. That is what happens when you believe even a very small point raised by your automatic brain—the thoughts that you'll find in box 2 and 3.

Since other situations now readily trigger Bernice's anger, we developed some methods for calming it. The first step, as I have mentioned, is controlled breathing. The initial response to the approach of anger should be a slow, deliberate breath in through the nose and out through the mouth. The second step is to say aloud, "I am taking a moment." (This is similar to taking a personal "time out," a technique I have used with my kids if I find myself getting angry; i.e., "*Dad's* going to take a time out right now.") Next comes the positive self-talk and affirmations.

I no longer believe and trust that my anger will guide and protect me. I believe 100 percent in the power of my mind to show me the way. I will always find a way and a way will always find me.

As I have shown, the direction of our automatic brain, is very persuasive, and draining. To put the wheels of change in motion, to achieve real survival—that is, a superior quality of life—one must not believe, trust, or take direction from the thoughts in boxes #2 and #3. Finding the power of our mind starts with believing, trusting, and taking direction from the thoughts that occupy box #1 and box #4—100 percent belief.

Of course, moving in the direction of one's true desires takes more than mantras and affirmations. Nevertheless, they can serve as the first line of strength to help block the automatic reflex, which acts to protect, yet ultimately sabotages. Not being aware of our automatic brain, allows it to run our daily lives. In the coming chapters, we will see that moving past the influences of our automatic brain will introduce us to a new world, a world that has been available to us since the day we were born. Yet it's a world that, because of the seductive and draining nature of our automatic brain, is not readily apparent. It's a world that connects us with a larger life force an indomitable power—the power of our mind—that helps us unite our earthly, practical experiences with a transcendent spirituality.

CHAPTER ELEVEN

Manipulation, Seduction,
and Lies

"The child is grown, the dream is gone, but I have become
comfortably numb."

–Roger Waters and David Gilmour (Pink Floyd)

It can be supremely liberating to first recognize and then accept that what controls the destiny of most people is the automatic brain. This revelation removes the blockade to the free flow between body, mind, and spirit. It stops the brain drain—the drain of our life force. It opens the door to understanding a deeper truth, a new world where our dreams and visions, our simple thoughts and ideas, can become manifest. It's a world where trust in something deeper than what our automatic brain determines to be real forms the energy, and hence power, that fuels us to attract into our lives that which is right for us. This world is almost entirely free of stress, and real danger is easy to recognize and remarkably rare.

This new world is right here on Earth.

The major difference between it and the one run by our automatic brain is that this new world opens up the possibility of wealth: spiritual wealth, physical wealth, emotional wealth, and yes, even that root of all evil (according to the falsities of the AB), financial wealth.

How do we live in this world? What does it look like? How do we get there?

As we have seen, the insidious nature of our automatic brain drums up persuasive thoughts or physical responses that pull us out of what it perceives to be dangerous territory. Alas, the realm of our AB takes in everything in our physical world—the world of our five senses. Anything our AB processes as less concrete or practical causes it to fire—to bring us back to our senses, so to speak.

But as we have also seen, the land of the AB is full of contradictions and fallacies. Although the automatic brain uses logic and reason to convince us to withdraw into a safe area, it relies mostly on thoughts, not tangible entities. These thoughts come from childish connections formed in the automatic brain as its memories—hence its data and proof. The past also presents a challenging irony. When our AB extracts from it proof why we should fight or flee, it automatically assumes that if things in the past went a certain way then our present would look a certain way. This, of course, is mere speculation. Likewise, the projections of future possibilities are pure fantasy, as that is the very nature of the future—an illusion that has yet to occur (in truth, make-believe). When we put our faith in this type of guidance, we end up nourishing our automatic brain, and perpetuating its misguided influence on our lives.

To begin moving away from the AB's influence on every aspect of our lives, we must first calm its robust activity. Without realizing it, we feed it constantly. The fight-or-flight mechanism activates anytime our automatic brain perceives events and situations as dangerous. When adrenaline stimulates our body and mind, the effect is brief unless we feed it.

Cutting off the AB's life source, its sustenance, is the best way to subdue its hold on our lives—the best way to stop the brain drain. As we have seen, the automatic brain will always be with us, and yes, we do need it on those rare occasions when real danger exists. But to prevent ourselves from being like the nervous little squirrel, darting and dodging, scurrying for a place to hide before the predator hawk swoops down and grabs it, we must cut off the constant control of our automatic brain. (If you doubt that it activates automatically, just wait for the next thunderstorm and see what happens when a clap of thunder awakens you from sleep. Even if you have gained some control over your automatic brain, it can reassert itself in an instant!)

In my own experience and in my discussions with patients, I have found that the primary nourishment of the automatic brain is any event that causes the AB to generate the statement, "Told you so!" Think of the AB as an overprotective parent—one who means well but ultimately is so fearful that something will happen to their child that they prevent the child from fleeing the nest (see Chapter 6). An overprotective parent will, by whatever means necessary, keep their child out of harm's way.

Sound familiar? Our automatic brains do the same thing. As I have said, often our behavior does not reveal the driving force behind it. (For example, when a couple argues because one of them does not screw the cap back on the tube of toothpaste, the capless tube is not the actual danger trigger for the anger and subsequent argument. It is something deeper within the relationship; for example, one person feeling the other doesn't respect them, overall.)

This may not sit well with some parents, but I have to point out that just as our AB misleads us into a false sense of security, so does being an overprotective parent. This kind of parent behaves this way in response to the automatic brain warning that if the child gets hurt, you are a bad parent, you are not worthy of the love of your parents or your spouse (love withdrawn = threat to survival), or the love of God (the ultimate judge). In order to avoid such crushing guilt (and make no mistake, guilt is another by-product of our protective AB), you, the parent, reel in your child.

In reality, the purpose of your overprotective actions is not to protect your child but to satisfy your automatic brain. This AB of ours uses manipulation, seduction, and lies—whatever it takes—to secure our child's safety; in actuality, our own safety. The child is an extension of our self, part of our legacy, our ticket to immortality, through our DNA (at least in the fabric of the automatic brain). Just think of the crazy thoughts that go through your head to lure you back to safety anytime you try to spread your wings. Our automatic brains are always seeking to pull us away from danger by generating thoughts that are clearly misrepresentations of the truth (manipulation), thoughts that promise a safer place (seduction), or downright mistruths (lying).

Take the example I used in Chapter 9. If I had whisked my daughter away from the starting line, would that have been for my safety, or hers? Since my duty is to protect her, to carry out my duty I should have "saved" her. In reality, my protecting her would be my automatic brain's definition of what a parent should be, which would in turn have been shaped by my own danger memories. Phew! In other words, "saving" her would be entirely to protect me.

As that overprotective parent, I might use manipulation, seduction, or lies to make my daughter think my actions are about her, but really, they would have been about my AB's need. Similarly, our automatic brain tries to make us think that we need it for protection, when in fact we rarely do. Following the lead of the AB can bring on paralysis. The more we listen to the manipulative, seductive, and untruthful thoughts generated by it, the more they paralyze us, drain us, and cause us to become comfortably numb in a place we don't want to be in.

One of the greatest lies is the thought, "See, I should have listened to my instinct and done (or not done) that." This kind of thought will inevitably occur if a negative event occurs while you are on your quest to believe in the power of your mind by removing the blockade of your automatic brain. The more you succumb to these thoughts, the more power you give your automatic brain. For example, in response to the story about my daughter, a patient said to me, "If your daughter had collapsed at the end of her race, you might have kicked yourself for not trusting your gut response to have the race canceled."

My answer touches on the metaphysical nature of our mind, which I will discuss later. Physical principals drive the automatic brain. Though it may rely on thoughts and projections as "proof," these derive from the fight-or-flight mechanisms designed to protect our physical body from danger. The triggered AB causes physical behaviors and responses (e.g., fighting aggressively or fleeing passively). And that's it—it cannot perform any other function except driving our behavior. Therefore, the image of a seizure from my automatic brain cannot manifest itself into my daughter's actually having a seizure. If she had a seizure, she had a seizure. The event could not be caused (by me) nor prevented. It just would have been.

When we rely on the thoughts generated by the automatic brain to make decisions, it often leads to a dead end. Although my automatic brain would have had me think that a seizure was the likely outcome (a lie), the more likely outcome—if I had listened to it and whisked her away or reprimanded the principal and teachers—would have been the embarrassment of my daughter and her general resentment toward me. Nevertheless, my AB told me that taking her out of harm's way would be an act of love...Hmm! In reality, the true harm comes from behaving according to the edicts of our automatic brain, believing, trusting, and taking direction from its barometer of danger. While taking its direction may prepare us for the worst-case scenario, the more we listen to it and feed it, the more it pushes away from our true desires and drains us of our life force and purpose. As we learn to believe, trust, and take direction from our mind, we manifest things and events that ring true for us.

Let's take Gloria as an example. Gloria is a 52-year-old successful executive and mother of two adult children. She came to me because she was concerned about developing dementia, about losing her mind. This was a central concern for her. We worked on developing a Revelation Grid, using the trigger of losing her mind.

I have found that people often cannot change a pattern of behavior or thought because they associate more danger with changing than with staying the same. As we worked on her grid, it became evident that the trigger to her automatic brain was actually *not* her fear of losing her mind. That concern was a sidelight masking the true issue – namely, that she *needed* to worry, whether it was worry about losing her mind or something else. The danger was in *not worrying* about something!

I explained that any trigger that is hard to identify probably stems from a locked-in childhood danger memory. Eventually, the revelation came. She said, "Since I was a child I would feel guilty if I didn't worry. My Mom to this day gets on my case, implying I'm not a good parent if I am not worrying. She says things like, 'What do you mean you didn't call? How do you know if they [Gloria's children] got there safely?' I learned from early on that if I don't worry, then I would wonder, what would happen to me now?"

The fact that Gloria can remember needing to worry from her early childhood means that the atmosphere around her house encouraged the need to worry, and that set up a danger memory of withdrawn love or poor esteem of her if she didn't worry. The connection that formed was that worry meant that her family would accept her as a good, caring, and compassionate person. The unspoken rule for being considered a caring person, and there-fore loved and respected, was to worry. The rule might have included the thought, "No child of mine is that cold and uncaring." By not living up to her parents' expectation (worrying), Gloria would not get their full measure of love. As I wrote in Chapter 7, an atmosphere like this is synonymous with death (to the impressionable, developing child's automatic brain, anyway). The familiar, "comfortable" environment of her childhood was one that cul-tivated and rewarded worry. Thus, a strong danger memory is formed.

Now in her 50s, if Gloria does not worry, her AB's automatic fight-or-flight thought is that some disaster will befall her or her family. The con-torted reasoning is that somehow she will be punished for not worrying. Her automatic brain is working to protect her from losing love because of being a cold, uncompassionate, non-worrying person. That is the power of the danger memory—the foundation of our omnipotent automatic brain.

As we identified Gloria's trigger, we could now formulate an accurate Glassman Revelation Grid and see how Gloria—like the rest of us—feed our automatic brain:

Circumstance/Trigger	Danger	Comfort/Safety
Worry	*Feel lousy all the time; feel stressed; wreck my health; loss of quality of life; alive but not really living.*	I know I'm doing everything I can to prevent the disaster.
Not worrying	The harm will come to pass; caught off guard; I will not have prepared or prevented it; disaster is certain.	

At first, Gloria said that she couldn't think of a positive thing to associate with not worrying—an entry for box #4. This, I explained, was symptomatic of a locked-in danger memory stemming from childhood. After I guided her a little, she began to open up with her own revelations of what life would be like without worry:

Circumstance/Trigger	Danger	Comfort/Safety
Worry	*Feel lousy all the time; feel stressed; wreck my health; loss of quality of life; alive but not really living.*	I know I'm doing everything I can to prevent the disaster; showing myself that I love my kids.
Not worrying	The harm will come to pass; caught off guard; I will not have prepared or prevented it; disaster is certain; kids will be in danger	*Living out of comfort zone in a place of serenity, where all is well and peaceful; I am at the top of my game mentally; I'm sharp and unafraid; no limit at my chances for success; I'm enjoying my family, because we have such a good time, my kids and I, when I let go of this stuff!*

Feeding the automatic brain means giving into the manipulation, seduction, and lies that it creates in its frantic efforts to keep us safe. The manipulation here would be "Harm will come to pass if I don't worry." The seduction is, "I will be viewed by my family as a better, loving person if I worry." And the lie is, "I can prevent danger if I worry."

When I asked Gloria where she would like to be, she admitted that box #4 was her true desire, but that she could not even think about being there because she feels "paralyzed by my history." It's the same way someone can be paralyzed by an overprotective parent. Moving in the opposite direction and abandoning the worry all at once is very difficult for Gloria because of the automatic brain's strong pull. Always in the background is the unspoken thought, "See I told you so; you should have listened to me." (Remember the example of the raincoat. If she decides to buck her overprotective parent or brain and not wear the raincoat, and then it rains, the "told you so" thought might arise). This, of course, is a lie; listening to the automatic brain does not cause things to be better. In this case, worrying would not cause Gloria's children to love her more, and it would not prevent disasters. But to abandon this state is frightening for her, because it is all she has known since childhood.

For Gloria to abandon her trust in her seductive automatic brain, and abandon her worry, would seem to be a monumental task. Recognizing that the automatic brain drives us is the first step to end the control it has over us. As with the example of Dr. John Forbes Nash, it, the automatic brain, is ever-present and is not going anywhere. When we stop believing, trusting, and taking direction from it we cut off its nourishment.

This all takes practice and persistence. Knowing that the AB is reflexive should prepare you for the thought that arises when something bad happens after you've followed my advice—something like "I tried following Glassman's theory and it didn't work for me." The automatic brain is reflexive and impatient. It always seeks to prepare you for the worst-case scenario, as it did for Gloria. It will fight to protect you from the spiritual and reflective nature of your mind through manipulative, seductive, and untruthful thoughts. I can only say that, as you continue to expose the true insincerity of your automatic brain, and thus stop feeding it, you will move closer to the power of your mind.

CHAPTER TWELVE

Food for Thought

Just when I think I'm out, they drag me back in again.

–Michael Corleone (Al Pacino), Godfather III

As we move away from our automatic brain's influence on our lives, situations arise that seem to drag us right back into its clutches. Through the manipulation, seduction, and lies, the AB remains quite persuasive as it operates 24/7 to "protect" us. Since it is so powerful and omnipresent, it doesn't need us continually to feed it. Even as we begin not to believe, trust, and take direction from the AB, many seemingly routine events drag us back and nourish it.

So how do we start to move away from our familiar place, i.e., the domain of the AB? How do we shield ourselves from the siren-call of our automatic brain, ever seeking to lure us back? The luring-back part can be very insidious and seductive; it may start with a little trickle, as the hole in the dike example, and quickly expand to an overwhelming flood.

The essential feeding grounds of our automatic brain exist in both the past and the future. This is where its resilience lies. As our thoughts drift into these areas, they lock us into a fraudulent and obsolete mechanism of protection and survival. Danger memories are false evidence and become our imperfect blueprint for planning future possibilities. The past is the fertile ground for the AB to plant its seed; the future its fertilizer. Repeatedly dwelling in these two areas feeds it, cultivates it, and makes you believe in it.

Recently, Francine (see Chapter 7) returned to my office. She expressed frustration that, even though she'd been successfully applying my techniques and ideas for weeks, every time she moved two steps forward she felt like events in her life were pulling her three steps back (I shared with her Michael Corleone's dilemma). Such is the nature of the automatic brain, I explained. As events unfold, our automatic brain measures them against stored danger memories and projects how these events will influence the future. Our AB manipulates us to the notion that somehow by doing this we'll get us to a safer, more favorable place.

Francine referred to recent rejections concerning her new business. "What could be good about that?" she asked. Her automatic brain responded to the events by measuring them against her past experiences and projecting their relevance to the future. What she came up with was reasons not to proceed with her business. I explained that by using the past and future as her reference points, she was believing, trusting, and taking direction from her automatic brain. And she indulged it; she fed it.

I explained that making decisions using a reference point of the *present* takes away the power of the automatic brain. Decisions she reaches in this way are more likely to move her where she wants to be—that is, into box #4 (see Chapter 9). I added that this does not remove the sense of reality of the event; it only puts it into perspective. The event is the event. The rejection is a rejection. That is what she faces here and now. The charge is not to allow our AB to judge, to determine the event to be dangerous.

I continued: "Allow me to say that whatever event is causing you to explode in anger or disappointment is bogus." Francine was puzzled. "But it is real, Dr. Glassman. I was rejected!" I explained, "Of course the *situation* is real, very real. But the *danger* that it implies is not real. The danger enters the equation only when your automatic brain calls on the past to judge the situation and look upon the future to project where it might lead. There is no danger in the moment. What happened in the past does not matter, what may happen in the future does not matter (since the future is a fantasy and illusion). Anything that points to danger (such as rejection) and prompts your anger is false. The situation is real; the danger is false. One-hundred percent belief in this will allow you to see solutions to your problems as if you are attracting those solutions. Labeling a circumstance as bad will indulge your AB and thereby establish an obstruction to seeing possibilities. That's what the AB does."

Once we allow our AB to judge a situation or event as dangerous, and we believe it, we successfully feed it and allow it to pull us into "safety" by manufacturing thoughts that pull us back or fight it. Francine's first tip-off that her automatic brain had judged an event dangerous was the reflex of anger. Anger is *always* a fight response of the AB, which means there is some danger that triggered it. The rejection as danger simply camouflaged her real danger trigger, which was the startup of her new business. Her automatic brain views all events that do not turn out the way she expects against this universal trigger. Since our automatic brain is constantly seeking to protect us, the reflex is often unexpected, but reliably automatic. If a situation makes her angry, she must recognize that it's simply her automatic brain "fighting" a dangerous situation. Allow the event to stand alone in the present.

"How then will I know if something is really dangerous?" Francine wondered. This automatic brain question comes from the false assumption that somehow we have to allow our automatic brain to plot our way to safety. I shared with her the story of another of my patients, Archie, who had been part of General George Patton's Third Army tank corps throughout World War II and during the D-Day invasion of France.

At 82, Archie can still vividly recall a day when he was 18. "The day was cloudy, a little misty. I drove; there was a gunner next to me and another gunner in the turret. As we rolled forward, we hit a minefield and received fire from all sides. Suddenly we must have hit a mine as the tank trembled and we were thrown around a bit, but not injured. The treads tore off the tank, and she caught fire. I was able to spring free [using an ejection device] and launched forward out of the tank.

"Along side the tank, while on the ground I suddenly felt a surge of heat through my upper right chest. A bullet had ripped through my chest. Still conscious, I collapsed and moved my left hand to my chest. The warm flowing blood engulfed my hand. I soon lost consciousness and the next thing I remember is waking up in some hospital-like area."

What kept Archie alive (besides the medics) was his automatic brain doing what it needed to do—get him to put his hand on the wound to slow the bleeding. He did not have to think about it. Enough adrenaline, and other stress hormones, and clotting factors pumped through his arteries and veins to reduce his hemorrhaging, maintain his blood pressure, and allow his buddies to help him flee the danger. And automatically and reliably, his automatic brain worked to protect his physical body.

Francine, just like the rest of us, is learning to recognize signs of her AB that drains our ability to realize our potential. When we need it, it will be there. We don't have to cater to its insatiable appetite.

Our ancestors of 50,000 years ago knew when danger lurked; the signs were obvious, and generally compelling. In some ways, very similar to what Archie experienced. For most of us, though, the constant flow of information presents us with many seeds to blossom and feed our automatic brain. The barrage of sensory input and information keeps our automatic brain on constant high alert.

One way to reduce the sense that danger is around from the moment we tumble out of bed in the morning is to filter the input. Most of us are news junkies. With the advent of 24-hour cable news, we are witness to the most horrific events, in real time. We are faced with a daily barrage of drive-by shootings, kidnappings, child molestation, fires, torture, bomb-ings, muggings, rapes, starvation, disease, murders, celebrity scandals, economic collapse, drownings, sexual harassment, discrimination, theft. Did I miss anything?

The pervasive sadness that surrounds most news reports works to feed our automatic brain. We begin to think horror and sadness are inevitably around every corner. Remember my experience with snorkeling, or watching my daughter's race? My automatic brain soaks up news about shark attacks and forms a danger memory that the risk of a shark attack is common. Similarly, all the horror stories about kids who engage in athletic competition suffering catastrophic illness or accidents add to the danger memory and provide a basis for the AB-protection machine.

News reports feed our automatic brain in two ways. First, they serve as evidence that we are in constant danger and need protection. Watching the news creates new danger memories and reinforces old ones. Second, the news creates a sense of hopelessness, a sense of having no control, perhaps based on reliance on old memories. The news of the day works to satisfy both requirements.

Some may argue that we need to be well informed to reduce the chance for all that horror, whether in our own lives or for those around us. My response is that this is an argument directly from the automatic brain. The sole purpose of our AB is to ensure our survival. Not relying on the AB or its vehicles (the news, for example), will allow your mind to be clearer and more apt to pick up the news that is relevant to your life.

The news has become the modern version of elevator music—it's constantly in the background, to the point where it numbs the automatic brain. This opens us up to a contradiction and falsity: We believe to protect ourselves we need more and more news information. The news becomes background noise that only makes us less aware and less alert. Thus, the more we rely on the AB, the less chance that we will ever come to know the power of his mind. The more we feed it, believe, trust, and take direction from it to "protect" us, the more stress we feel and the harder it becomes to be optimistic. One way to begin starving the AB is to be selective about what we listen to or read. News programs often dwell on tragedy as a way to draw in viewers, constantly upping the ante as our AB gets more desensitized. I suggest not viewing any news programs that operate with this type of agenda. Most nightly news programs are notorious for this, and at the risk of losing their support for my book, I suggest you tune them out! When you're in the car, avoid listening to all-news radio. During their broadcasts, human tragedy becomes a 30-second sound bite. A double homicide is mixed in with a report on the winner of the Coney Island hot dog eating contest.

Your automatic brain makes you believe that you need these stories to be well informed and remain sensitive. The reality is that you will be more sensitive to human suffering if you avoid the daily barrage. When you change the channel and hear of a terrorist attack in Bali or an earthquake in China, do not stop to hear how many people have died or how many children have been left homeless. Fixating on the story feeds your automatic brain. The mere knowledge of such devastation gives us enough information to act, in a manner we choose. Knowing every detail about these events only feeds the automatic brain.

To stay informed, I suggest becoming selective about the news you expose yourself to. When I go to an online news site, I pick and choose the stories at which I look. Headlines that do not focus on human pain and suffering are the ones I will likely open up to read. I may see the headlines about those things, but I will not read further for the gruesome details. To do so would be to give into the instinct and reflex of the automatic brain. News reports serve to stimulate the one-up trigger—they make *my* life not appear so bad. Feeling one-up signals the AB that it's in a safer place—having the advantage over others, therefore not threatened by them.

On the other hand, when we let the AB drive us, the notion of someone having it better than us triggers the fight-or-flight response. (No wonder we feel stressed all the time!) This is another method by which the news media feeds our automatic brain. Someone else having what we think we want signals danger.

Envy is a passive response (the flight), and the Germans have a word describing the aggressive response (the fight) - *Schadenfreude*. The word derives from *Schaden* (damage, harm) and *Freude* (joy). It means finding enjoyment in another's misfortune. Most of us don't like to think that we could be so cruel; however, schadenfreude helps explain why some shows (news and reality) and magazines are so popular. A study, appearing in the February 2009 edition of the journal *Science*, revealed that a pleasure area of our brain (likely a part of what I call the automatic brain), actually is very active when one experiences schadenfreude.

You may know of politicians who take advantage of our instinct for schadenfreude by portraying anyone who has more than us as sinister, deceitful, or even criminal. The automatic brain often holds that certain groups corner the market for ethics, morality, or good will or the converse. We should not feed it and single out any particular socioeconomic group, racial, or religious group as the reason we are not where we wish to be. If we are not where we wish to be, it is because we follow and feed our automatic brain.

That does not mean you and I are bad people. Our automatic brain is designed to help us survive. In prehistoric times it served us quite well, but in the present day, perceived danger is so pervasive that our fight-or-flight response shows up in unpredictable ways. To end its grip on us—that is, not get rid of it but gain control over it—we must stop feeding it. That's why I suggest you avoid all those grim news stories, together with coverage of things like hedge-fund managers facing prosecution, celebrities getting divorced or in rehab and gossip in general, which serve to strengthen the schadenfreude reflex.

(Of course, avoiding news stories is easier than avoiding gossip. You can ignore the news by simply switching the station or skimming through a newspaper or magazine. But when someone approaches you with gossip, you don't want to seem rude. Instead, just let the subject run out of steam by not asking questions or by politely changing the subject).

When you find yourself experiencing feelings of envy (the root of all gossip) or you recognize a certain satisfaction over the misfortune of another, that should be a signal that your focus is shifting—away from your own strengths. You are feeding your AB. Therein lies another contradiction: These stories automatically draw you in to give you more protective ammunition—to make you feel superior and in a less dangerous place. But when you do, you actually magnify your weaknesses and deplete your strength by fixating on someone else's strengths. One of the ways the AB protects us is by distracting us from our own life and concentrating on someone else's. After all, who is more likely to threaten your survival, you or someone else? The primitive nature of our automatic brain is on constant alert for the latter. That is precisely why stories of others draw us in, and it is another inherent deception of the automatic brain.

I want to say a bit more about moving in the opposite direction of the automatic brain. When you feel like sitting back and relaxing after a hard day's work by turning on the local news…don't! When you are in your car and you tune to an all-news radio station, tune somewhere else—perhaps music or, if you have satellite radio, a comedy. When you find yourself attracted to the misfortune of others for your entertainment, move in the opposite direction. Do not believe, trust, or take direction from this instinct. It will keep you stuck, bouncing between box #2 and box #3. If you enjoy juicy gossip, try to move in the opposite direction. You may get some questions and raised eyebrows from your friends, which could trigger danger. Instead of fleeing this type of danger and giving in to the gossip, give your friends a copy of my book! It's a way of gaining control of your automatic brain so you control it, rather than it controlling you.

A less obvious way we feed our automatic brain is through the judgments we make. We all judge, and the automatic judgments we make are yet another example of how our AB operates to protect us. How many times have you been in a public place—a supermarket, say—and with everyone you pass you find yourself assessing how they are dressed, for instance, moving quickly to what their life must be like. The thoughts appear automatically.

What do you think about when you see someone driving a fancy, expensive car? What goes through your mind if the driver cuts you off? We seem to be in the habit of constantly sizing people up. This reflex protects us from potential violators of our space, but unfortunately, as with the other features of our AB, the resulting generalized, over-exaggerated reaction has little to do with reality. So much is going through our minds when we cross paths with someone that we do not recognize his or her real essence. First impressions are frequently the only chance we have to make an impression, but when we interact with people in our daily lives, first impressions are much less vital. Our judgments serve only to feed our automatic brain, to insulate us from "danger", to jockey for position.

The most reassuring aspect to all of this is that while you are forming these fleeting judgmental thoughts about people you encounter, they too are having thoughts about you, as they too have an automatic brain that's attempting to shield them. Reflexive judgments come from the automatic brain; reflective judgments are from your mind. The trick is to distinguish between what's reflexive and what's reflective. The reflective part of your brain evaluates the reflex thoughts to determine whether there's a need for protection. This part is easy, as there are few circumstances in our everyday lives where we really need to be judgmental. The reflective process is, in a way, a matter of taking a step back from yourself and evaluating the types of judgments you are making.

What happens if instead of being reflective we act on reflexive judgments? For one thing, we tend to look for others to share and validate our judgments, giving rise to gossip, and providing fodder for the AB.

The thoughts that creep into your brain about other people tell you less about those people you are judging than they do about yourself. Your judgments can help you expose the types of thoughts that control you. Here's an exercise I suggest to help you become aware of your automatic judgmental thoughts: Make a note of the type of judgments you make. Start by writing down a list of judgments you make during one day. You will probably notice a trend. For instance, you may automatically judge another person's appearance (fit or fat, neat or unkempt). Or your judgments may relate to people you perceive as wealthier than you (e.g., self-centered rich snob born with a silver spoon in his mouth). Make a list of all your judgments and perceptions that are reflexive. Then sit down and become reflective. Think about what your opinions mean as they relate to how you feel about yourself and your own abilities. Now see if any of these judgments and your opinions of yourself show up in some form in box #2 or box #3. I bet they will. These are what keep us under the control of the automatic brain.

Avoiding the one-upmanship syndrome is another way to cut off the food supply to the AB. Someone you're having a conversation with may say something about him or herself, or may mention some possession or pending vacation plans, for example. That may prompt you to come back with something better about yourself or withdrawal passively as you flee the 'danger" of being one-upped. But resist the temptation and simply move in the opposite direction. Engaging in one-upmanship is one of the most insidious faces of the fight (aggressive) reflex that feeds the AB. Ultimately, though, giving in to this behavior starves you and prevents you from reaching your desired place.

No discussion on feeding the AB would be complete without a discussion of real food—eating. Our automatic brain drives us to fight or to flee danger. In order to do this, we need quick energy to support our brain, muscles, and other vital organs. To supply this, our body needs to have a lot of sugar available to convert into energy. Cellular respiration is the process by which our cells use oxygen and sugar to create energy. As our automatic brain perceives danger and the fight-or-flight physical response and thinking begin, the need for oxygen and sugar increases. Part of our automatic brain is responsible for our craving of sugar and fatty foods (the latter is stored so it can later be broken down into sugar for energy).

Insulin—familiar to all diabetics—is the hormone required to shift sugar out of the blood and into cells, so the cells can convert it to energy. Picture a lock on the door to all our cells. To open this lock we need a key to let in blood sugar. That key is insulin. Insulin also converts excesses of sugar, beyond what the cells need for immediate energy, into fat. Sugar is the only substance the brain uses for energy. When we eat sugar, it gives us a surge of energy and a generalized feeling of well being. This is short lived, as a burst of insulin follows our intake, unlocking the door to our cells, letting sugar in, ultimately lowering the levels of sugar in our blood.

This sugar/insulin cycle resembles common addiction patterns to all drugs, including alcohol, cocaine, tobacco, and even heroin. The surge of energy and well feeling is addicting. As it wears off, we have learned what it takes to get that feeling back again; that is, to eat more of the food that gave us that feeling. Thus, the automatic brain encourages us to eat more sugar and fat to feed it more.

Our craving for sugar and fat is present at birth, and for our ancestors, that craving was essential for survival. But what use does it have now? We still require a minimal amount of sugar and fat to survive, but things have changed. Now, we are destined to be less healthy if we are not aware that the craving for sugar and fat is seducing us. Our automatic brain tells us that we need that food for survival. Just as the automatic brain causes us to become addicted to certain behaviors, we actually become addicted to giving in to the manipulation, seduction, and lies it dishes out to us. Listening to our AB causes us to become addicted to sugar and fat, and ultimately decreases our life expectancy. In short, instead of helping us survive, our sugar and fat addiction does the opposite.

Nonetheless, just as not everyone who enjoys the occasional decadent chocolate cake with ice cream is addicted to food, we too may indulge the AB now and then, but under our terms. This starts with an awareness of what is motivating us. Suffice it to say, constant eating beyond sustenance levels, i.e., what you really need to survive, is a tip off that you may be driven by your automatic brain's manipulations.

The search for why we feel stressed all the time, or why we constantly feel pessimistic, is not so difficult once we realize that we're constantly feeding the very root of our discontent. In order to move our life in the direction of a higher truth, and make manifest our true desires, and not succumb to brain drain, we must recognize where the automatic brain's sustenance comes from, whether the past, future, or its misinterpretations of events in the present. As we accomplish this, we will move toward a life of true abundance where the flow of possibility runs limitlessly from our powerful mind.

PART II

The Power of Our Mind

CHAPTER THIRTEEN

Stopping Brain Drain: Discovering the Power of the Mind

*"The universal Mind contains all knowledge.
It is the potential ultimate of all things. To it, all things are possible."*

–Ernest Holmes

Removing our belief and trust in the automatic brain unleashes the ability to experience the power of our mind. But what is this mind exactly?

The term *mind-body connection* is often used to describe phenomena that are not clearly explained by medical science, not clearly explained by the automatic brain. The term is not brain-body connection, but refers to the distinct association between our physical body and a possible source of profound power and influence. Whereas the automatic brain simply works to restrict and protect our body, our mind propels us with an understanding that we are safe beyond the limits of our physical environment, which includes our body. Not only are we safe, but we are in a position to tap into energy that rests beyond our sensory awareness.

Our mind intersects with our physical reality in many areas. It is responsible for the apparent acts of superhuman strength sometimes observed when we're placed in a life-or-death situation. Spontaneous remission from disease is another example of the power of our mind. The placebo effect is yet another manifestation of the influence of our mind, as I described in the introduction.

The physical manifestation of the mind lies somewhere deep within our neocortex. As we learn to tap into our mind for guidance, we overcome the obstruction of the automatic brain, thus attracting everything that is right for us. You see, many who have talked about the law of attraction assume falsely that we have the ability to attract harm into our lives as well as abundance. Rather, we must understand that when we believe, trust, or take direction from the automatic brain we fail to realize the powerful attractive force of our mind, our access to great spiritual energy. Therefore, we fail to recognize our innate incalculable ability to create abundance. It is not that we attract bad things, it is just that we do not recognize what is already part of us—the power of our mind. Simply said, we don't attract bad, we just realize less good. The automatic brain serves as the single greatest obstruction to this realization.

Our mind helps us connect with the metaphysical concept of universal energy, power, and divine guidance—something we all have the ability to achieve.

My journey to find the power of my mind began many years ago. As a child, I remember being fascinated by the concept of infinity. How could something have no identifiable beginning or end? This mystery led me to believe that there must be something greater than what we can see, hear, touch, smell, or taste (technically, there are other senses as well—like position sense—but these too are physical and finite).

Throughout my younger years, I was exposed to religion, attending Hebrew school and having my Bar Mitzvah at an Orthodox Jewish synagogue. As I got older, I began to realize that certain aspects of my traditional religion did not feel right to me. I began thinking of myself as spiritual rather than religious. Traditional religion seems to indulge the automatic brain. Now, I certainly respect those who believe in religious laws, but religious law, it seems to me, actually prevents us from a truer understanding of, and relationship with, God and what I see as the divine portal—our mind.

I have said that our AB is very persuasive, as it needs to be, in order to protect our physical body. I believe this persuasion has contributed to the creation of traditional religion as we know it. As I wrote in the first chapter, the AB prevents us from understanding our connection to our spiritual self and having an authentic relationship with God.

My first experience with my inner guidance—that is, my connection with my mind—happened at the end of my freshman year at Hobart College in Geneva, New York, when I was 18 years old. Briefly, it was a hot Tuesday evening in early June in a non-air-conditioned classroom in a 60-year-old brick building. I was struggling through a particularly difficult final exam in Linear Algebra. This was the last exam of the trimester. Although I was a good math student, I always needed the whole time to finish an exam; I never finished early. But for some reason, with this extremely difficult exam, I did finish early.

As I squirmed restlessly in the narrow wooden chair, I was anticipating the upcoming summer vacation. I glanced over the problems in front of me one last time, feeling confident that "I aced this one." From nowhere, an inner voice directed me to check the last problem. As if something outside myself was guiding me, my pencil moved through the problem from beginning to end, correcting errors and finally arriving at a solution that was completely different from my previous result!

The professor later informed me that I was the only one who got that last problem right. More importantly, this was my first encounter with what I now think of as my inner guidance. No, the skies did not open and I did not see angels. I just know that my performance on the exam was the manifestation of the power of my mind.

For years, I tried to find the same sort of guidance again, but my automatic brain continued to be very active. Often I did not like the signals I got from my AB, so I looked for ways to squelch it. That led me, in my first year of medical school, to begin training in karate, which I would continue for the next 12 years. In addition to the familiar physical moves,

I practiced various breathing and meditation techniques. And also in that class, I met the woman who would become my wife.

Karate gave me certain physical and mental skills that I found very valuable in calming my automatic brain and glimpsing the power of my mind. The concept of willpower, indeed of will itself, is a vehicle of the mind. The mind, after all, is the purest form of free will, since it is not limited by the automatic brain. Willpower is simply not allowing the automatic brain to direct our behavior. It is a deeper belief in our self, the power of our mind.

Several years after beginning karate, I connected with the power of the mind on a more tangible level—the kind of connection I was seeking.

After the blood pressure incident I described back in Chapter 6, I found myself reading books on relaxation. One in particular greatly influenced me: *The Relaxation Response*, by Herbert Benson, MD. Benson described his research on Himalayan monks—how they were able to control physical functions previously considered not controllable by the conscious brain, like body temperature, heart rate, and blood flow to certain organs. His book reminded me of a lecture I had had in medical school that included actual footage of such "impossibilities."

It was striking to me that these monks could gain control of automatic processes through mind control, willpower, and focus. The video I had watched in med school and the findings of the researchers were not part of some smoke-and-mirrors magic trick. So I wondered if monks were the only people capable of such feats. I decided that they weren't. Their capabilities exemplify how we can channel the power of the mind to affect our body.

Dr. Benson suggested a plan to help non-monks like me develop control over automatic reflexes. He described a meditation technique, which I began to practice during my final year of residency. This took place about four years after the events in Chapter 6. (I will describe the meditation process in detail in a later chapter.)

During meditation, as I would go deeper into it, I'd visualize myself traveling downward on an elevator. As the elevator stopped its descent, the doors opened. In front of me (in my mind) I saw a meadow. To my left was a rock surrounded by a grassy field and a large tree just beyond the rock in the center of my field of mental vision. The large meadow extended off in the distance to the right, and reminded me of a scene from *The Wizard of Oz*.

On the rock stood a small man. He hopped off the rock and introduced himself as Abe. The voice with which Abe spoke to me was familiar: It was the inner voice from years before, during my math exam.

From that point on, I meditated for about 20 minutes, once or twice a day. Whenever I encountered "Abe," we would stroll together. I found myself seeking answers from him to help me know my future. I practiced this for a few months, but eventually drifted away from the experience. I think what happened was that I began listening to the edicts of my automatic brain that classified this kind of activity as crazy and impractical. In any case, I abandoned my attempts at trying to connect with Abe. Perhaps I was not getting the results that I had expected. Maybe I decided he wasn't giving me accurate information about the future—after all, Abe didn't supply me with the winning lottery numbers! I continued with karate, but my connection with Abe, my inner guide, seemed to have faded.

But then, in the summer of 2004, Abe came back into my life. That summer my wife was diagnosed with breast cancer. The biopsy result came two days before our summer vacation, which we were going to spend with close friends. The day before we left, the doctor scheduled the follow-up definitive and diagnostic surgery for the following month. Also that day, I meditated in the fashion I had 20 years earlier. And Abe was right where I had left him.

What he told me was that everything that mattered was right here, now, in the moment, in the present. In that present moment, on that day, my wife was with our family and me. Abe guided me to focus on each moment, each day. He guided me not to speculate about the uncertainties of the future. Though Abe did not comment specifically on the future, at the end of each meditation over the next two months, he said, "And by the way, everything is going to be OK." What "OK" was, he did not say. The overwhelming sense I got was that everything was going to be OK, no matter what. This powerful guidance neutralized the urgings of my automatic brain. During our vacation, we did not share the diagnosis with our friends, or our children. We had a wonderful vacation.

On the day of the surgery, I was very anxious. My automatic brain was again active and, as my wife went into the operating room, projections about the future and memories of the past were flying through my brain. As I sat in the waiting room, I looked at magazines and watched television, but did not see or hear anything. I thought the surgery would be quick, but it lasted over an hour, which made me think that they found something more.

As the surgeon approached me, I felt like my heart was pounding in my throat. The doctor told me she had gotten the whole tumor the first time and the lymph nodes were negative. The thing is, I felt she would say that—I *knew* she would say that. Yet my automatic brain had steered me through the past and future into a very dark place. For the most part, during the month leading up to the surgery, I had meditated, and listened to my inner guidance. But on that day, at least up until the surgeon's reassurance, my automatic brain controlled me.

What if she had told me that the tests *weren't* negative? Would that have invalidated my inner guidance? My inner guidance told me that everything would be OK. For this time around, "getting it all" is what "OK" meant. Perhaps if I had not listened to my inner guidance—or my wife not listened to hers—we would have been controlled by a vortex of fear, canceled our vacation, told the world of our misery, and thus painted a picture in which no matter what the surgical result, everything would *not* be OK. But by listening to Abe, no matter what the diagnosis, *it would be OK.*

My wife's experience influenced me to look at myself and my career. Throughout the next year, I began to focus more on areas of medicine in which I'd always been interested, but which were outside my normal practice. Some of the topics included anti-aging medicine, complementary medicine, and the mind-body connection. My new interests led me to leave a partnership of 17 years and launch a solo practice. In my mind, I had completed a revelation grid before knowing what one was. During that time, though, I gradually phased out the meditation and my encounters with Abe. (Such is the influence of the automatic brain).

When I began distributing my weekly messages at the beginning of 2007, some of my patients recommended books to me that they felt reflected my point of view. One book showed up on several of the recommendation lists: *The Secret*. I found that many of the ideas in this best-selling work relating to "the law of attraction" rang true for my life. After watching the DVD and reading the book, I resumed my practice of meditation again. And as I had hoped, Abe was there to meet me, nonjudgmental as ever.

As I sought out more information on this interesting law of attraction idea, I came across the writings of Esther Hicks, especially *The Teachings of Abraham*. Her description of her first encounter with the presence she calls "Abraham" sounded eerily familiar to my first encounter with Abe (whether the similarity of names is a coincidence, I'll let you be the judge). Here I was, some 23 years after I first met Abe, and I was hearing someone describe a similar encounter. This began to feed my belief and trust in the power of the mind—my inner guide as the portal to a greater spiritual force.

For the next few months, I meditated about three or four days per week. During each experience, I met and talked with my inner guidance.

In the summer of 2007, I had the inspiration to develop another business, outside my private practice. The business would provide corporations with wellness education, addressing stress, nutrition, and fitness.

For almost a year, I worked on this project with a partner. We developed what I believed to be a program that was both dynamic and positioned for growth.

But in May 2008, my partner, for personal reasons, decided she could no longer go forward with the business. She called me on a Saturday morning to discuss this, and we agreed to end our business. Just like that, almost a year of work went down the drain. That morning I felt a little sad. This melancholy mood lasted about two hours. I took a shower and began my meditation. As I drifted deep into meditation, I met Abe in his usual place. The meditation lasted particularly long, nearly 25 minutes. What stands out most from it is what my inner guidance directed: "*Turn your weekly messages into a book*," "*You don't need anyone but yourself*," and "*Meditate every day*."

Thus was the birth of my book. As I wrote each chapter, Abe guided me. I know that my trust and belief in my inner guidance is much truer and more real than anything generated by my automatic brain. Yet the reality of our physical world is so persuasive and its grip so relentless that to put 100 percent trust in a concept as intangible as a little man named Abe appears, I guess, crazy.

Believing in the power of our mind, I should add, is different from putting your life in the hands of chance. It is different from giving your life over to an imaginary father figure in the sky. The mind is your deepest connection with the universe and God and the mystery that surrounds everything that occupies most of what we define as physical matter. It confirms your uniqueness, yet stands with all humanity as a singularity. Connecting with our mind allows the free flow of energy between mind, body, and spirit—attracting what is right for us. It reminds us that most of the direction from our automatic brain is composed of fallacies, not the least of which is the fact that the surrounding space, which we see as physical, is actually emptiness. Fully understanding this helps us live with the mind, rather than the AB, as our guide. We can then make real the intangibility of mind, affecting relationships, material belongings, physical health, and physical pleasure.

My belief in the power of the mind is certainly compatible with traditional religion, though for me it fills a void left by traditional religion. For example, I now more clearly understand the idea of prayer. Prayer in its purest form is active meditation. It is stepping beyond the limits of the five senses and reaching out to a power greater than our AB can comprehend. It is a humble admission that what we think we know is not all there is. The universe as we know it is mostly empty space. For instance, if you were to place the nucleus of an atom in the center of a large football stadium, the outer orbiting electrons would be in the last row in the nosebleed section. All the space in between is empty. That emptiness is what makes up everything we see, feel, touch, smell, and taste. What we think we know as skin and bones is mostly nothingness. Albert Einstein predicted—correctly, as it was later shown—that this nothingness contains enormous energy. Through the meditative activity of prayer, the power of our mind serves as a portal to a much greater source of energy—a force, a spirit, what some call God.

Some of us believe that we are created in the Lord's image. I believe that image cannot be made of flesh and bones but must be something more. That something more is the spirit or image that lives within every one of us—our mind as the conduit to a divine energy force.

Thanks to meditation, I now understand how important it is to believe in this inner force—to believe that it is a more reliable source of strength and guidance than our AB and is somehow connected with the divine force.

Many of us look to places of worship to find and connect with divinity, whether we call it that or not. We attend churches or synagogues or mosques, and pray to God. Then we transport ourselves back into the "real" world, and any holy connection we've achieved quickly fades into a sea of earthly realities. This is due to the persuasions—the manipulation, seduction, and lies—of the automatic brain. Believing in the power of our mind removes the obstruction of the AB, stops brain drain, and fosters a resilient faith.

For anyone who's learned how to believe, trust, and take direction from the power of the mind, the fear of death that hangs over most people's lives is no longer present, because physical death means only death of the automatic brain. Indeed, the possibility of death is the very thing that supplies fodder for our AB, because it is the thing from which our AB tries to protect us.

When we are guided by our mind, there is room for financial wealth, healthy vibrant bodies, and strong, exciting relationships. Thus, some of what is right for us exists clearly within the material world, and the AB may try to confuse us into thinking that we cannot exist in both a world created by the automatic brain and one created by the mind. However, if these are manifestations of our mind rather than our AB, certain achievements actually reaffirm our connection with the deeper truth, and can serve as an example of the power of this internal and universal force. Next, I will show how we manifest what is right for us; how it becomes important to us, and how we know it came from our mind.

CHAPTER FOURTEEN

The Right Choice

❧❧❧❧❧

"We must make the choices that enable us to fulfill the deepest capacities of our real selves."

–Thomas Merton

I recall during my medical school rotation in behavioral science, the doctors felt that one of the schizophrenic patients was getting worse because of his paranoid delusions that the FBI was closing in on him. Imagine their surprise when none other than the FBI showed up at the doors of the ward. It turned out he had been writing threatening letters to the President. Remember our favorite schizophrenic, John Forbes Nash, whom I discussed in a previous chapter. Dr. Nash had three primary delusions: a little girl for whom he acted as a role model, a rambunctious college buddy to whom he could be a best friend, and an FBI agent who needed him for secret projects. These were all delusions Dr. Nash created with his automatic brain. All shared a common theme: His automatic brain created them to protect him, to boost him up, to make him feel larger than others, thus satisfying the AB's need to be above others so as not to be annihilated.

We might watch *A Beautiful Mind* or hear about the schizophrenic patient above and feel glad that we are not so crazy. The fact is, though, the only difference between the schizophrenic and us is that the thoughts generated by the AB in the former case are more vivid and creative. Among the many theories of this disabling disease, one theory by

Gregory Bateson, known as the double-bind theory, still has some legs, so to speak. The essential hypothesis of the double-bind theory is that 'victims'—the people who become psychotically unwell—find themselves in an environment in which messages contradict each other but they can't communicate that contradiction. For that reason, the unwell person is unable to escape the condition of confusion (remember the grandmother in Chapter 8). Because of its constant activity and its resolute drive, schizophrenia tries to prevent the individual from ever escaping its grip.

I have shown that most of the thoughts that come from our automatic brain are false and not to be believed. The difference between those false thoughts and schizophrenic delusions is that we have the ability to recognize that they are false whether we acknowledge it or not. Through medication, Dr. Nash was eventually able to recognize that the delusions of his automatic brain were fallacies too, and, while acknowledging that they would forever be present, he was able to find the purer truth found in his mind.

As one connects with their inner guidance, they inevitability will have conversations in their mind. The voices of the mind are not delusions. When we stop believing, trusting, and taking direction from the AB, solutions to challenges and answers to perplexing questions seem to come into our mind spontaneously, effortlessly. When we stop brain drain, we unleash the power of the mind.

Recently I completed a revelation grid with Martin, who was having a good deal of difficulty in social situations. He urgently wanted to find comfort in being with people and not being alone; nevertheless, his grid revealed that social situations triggered his automatic brain and treated being alone as a comfort or safe zone.

His revelation grid looked like this:

Circumstance/Trigger	Danger	Comfort/Safety
Not being social (being alone)	*No one to rely on; angry about it; resent others having what I can't get; being lonely without companionship; no future.*	Nobody to judge me; no pressure; no expectations; no judgment; staying in a familiar, safe, comfortable place.
Being social (not being alone)	What I fear most about what people are going to say about what I say or what they're going to think (so I end up holding everything in); I don't want to offend anyone with things I might say; might hurt someone's feelings; afraid of what others are going to think of me.	*Someone to support me; validation of points of view; exchange ideas; companionship; nurturing.*

As I continue to work with Martin, he bounces back and forth between the AB thoughts of boxes 2 and 3. Constantly, he insists that box 4 is where he wants to be. But he feels that he is in denial if he does not listen to his automatic brain. I pointed out (and this applies to everyone who completes a revelation grid) that the only denial is denying the fact that his true desires rest within box 4. Even though the AB will spare no effort to make him believe the safe way to think is in boxes 2 and 3, not trusting, believing, and taking direction from his true desires is the ultimate denial—the ultimate delusion.

Money is the greatest manipulator of the automatic brain, yet also can be the greatest manifestation of the power of the mind in our physical world. Using money, the AB manipulates in two ways: either with thoughts like, "Money is the root of all evil," or with belief that money will make us more powerful, respected, loved, happy. When I decided to become a doctor, I felt that if I were sincere in my work, money would come without my having to try to scrounge for it. We all know what happened with managed care, forcing me to be more creative in my sincerity to myself and my work. As I write this book, my mind tells me that it will make money, because I am writing it from the power of my mind. Money will be one manifestation of that. Money becomes part of the process, not the motivator nor the goal. It just is. It is not the cause of your actions, but the effect. It remains a commanding, tangible symbol of the power of our mind.

How the power of our mind reveals its presence in our lives may at first seem to blend with the automatic brain. But let's review a few concepts. The automatic brain is quite simple, in the sense that it operates solely to ensure our survival through the fight-or-flight response. The fight-or-flight response shows up in our lives mostly as aggressive and passive behaviors, respectively. Martin, the patient I referred to above, is responding passively through withdrawal, because social situations represent a threat to him. Another example: Remember Tom from Chapter 7? Tom far surpassed his parents' wealth. Even now, they make half-joking remarks to him about it. But his real danger memory was implanted by growing up in a home where wealth was regarded as something negative. In order to continue to receive his parents' love, he needed to echo them in trashing the wealthy, and certainly could not aspire to wealth for himself. Now that he is, in fact, one of them, the danger memory gets continually triggered. Being different from his parents and not needing their help is tantamount—in his automatic brain, at least—to losing their love. In a real sense, it represents a threat to his survival. Moving beyond the familiar comfort zone of wealth bashing is dangerous and hence life-threatening.

Now let's fast-forward to Tom's current life situation. Tom and his wife recently purchased a boat and a Mercedes sedan. As you have no doubt figured out, by doing so, he triggered a danger memory; in other words, a show of wealth means Tom is becoming one of the wealthy that his parents so resented and whom they associated with something bad. Any danger will trigger the automatic brain and leads to fight-or-flight thoughts and/or behavior. In this case, aggressive behavior (fight) would be Tom's bragging incessantly about his purchases; making every attempt to bring them up in conversation with others or going out of his way to be noticed driving his new car. Passive behavior (flight) would be that Tom has to think every time he is going to drive his car, whether or not he will make someone feel bad who does not have what he has. Or feel embarrassed about inviting anyone on the boat for the danger that he may be discovered as "one of them" (i.e. the cheating rich people).

What Tom and I have worked out is the idea of reacting assertively—the behavior displayed when one follows the direction of the mind. This came about because Tom felt uncomfortable with his purchases, and that led to stress mostly through a passive (flight) response, causing him to feel uneasy anytime someone who did not have what he had noticed him in his car. I helped him realize that the fact that many of his neighbors had similar possessions did not influence his decision making. He did not make the decision to obtain these items because he was trying to one-up the Jones family. He purchased a boat because he loves the water, always dreamed of having one, loves the freedom he feel while on it. As for the Mercedes, the truth is, most of the time you get what you pay for. He and his wife love the drive, the interior comfort, the safety, and the way it looks. As we say in medicine, true, true, and unrelated: true his neighbors had similar possessions, true he just bought a boat and fancy car, but the two events are unrelated.

I coached Tom that he could not be responsible for others' automatic brains and how they might judge him. Other people can act as external automatic brains as they blindly follow their AB and impose judgment upon another. Just as I urged Tom not to believe, trust, or take direction from his own automatic brain, I equally encouraged that he not slip into the tendency to listen to the judgments of others; whether perceived or real. The sincerity of his mindful decision has allowed Tom to begin feeling comfortable with his success. Not only does he allow his success just to 'be' without any past or future implications attached to it, he also puts himself in a better position to attract more. He no longer is drained by his automatic brain's self-sabotaging decrees.

Recently, a pharmaceutical representative in my office approached me during a particularly busy time. This imposition was enough to activate my automatic brain, and I felt a bit of stress as the fight-or-flight response kicked in—as expected when an unwelcome visitor infringes on another's space. Not being aware of this might have led me to be aggressive (fight) and reprimand the rep for bothering me, or try to one-up the rep by showing that my knowledge of the drug was better than hers. Or I might have become passive (flight) and allowed her to give me a five-minute drug pitch when I did not have a second to spare.

Whether one fights or flees, the effect on the body, mostly through the release of adrenaline and cortisol, is the same: stress. In this instance, the mindful approach is to act assertively, which I did—I simply explained that this was not a good time. I did not get aggressive and I did not passively yield to the request that I really did not wish to grant.

How many times do you face similar situations in your daily life with your boss, your co-workers, your spouse, your children? Are you aware that something in this interaction is alerting your AB to danger and that fight-or-flight behavior or thoughts are developing? Once you recognize this, you begin to find the real power, which exists in your mind.

The ability to recognize the motivation for one's behavior is the first step in making mindful decisions. What if AB-based behaviors end up in acts that seem, on the surface, good? After all, what could be wrong with Angelina Jolie's compassion for orphaned African children? Or a PTA president's enthusiasm? Or a politician's passion to change the world? All are fight responses to a trigger from a danger memory yet to be discovered by the individual. In other words, all are results of the automatic brain.

Good or bad, continually acceding to this driver will end unsatisfactorily, in the long run, for the individual and for anyone they are apparently helping. This is not to say that people who adopt, PTA presidents, and politicians are incapable of mindful decision-making .

AB-based decision-making is more evident when there is a strong need to be recognized as a "do-gooder." For instance, someone who aspires to be a PTA president to out-shine another person or to be recognized as a good person is acting from the automatic brain. Remember, the automatic brain decides when survival is in jeopardy. So to appear above or better than others limits that threat. Mindful-based decisions and choices just stand alone, without any baggage, without any threat. They are genuine. They are true instinct and are always right. But I'm not pretending to stand in judgment. It is up to individuals to evaluate if the automatic brain orchestrates their primary motivation. This usually takes honest introspection and the completion of a Revelation Grid. It takes a sincere acknowledgement that one is not immune to the powerful influence of the automatic brain. Many people who wish to be viewed as good, do so precisely to hide the reality that their automatic brains are uncomfortably influential in their lives. To position oneself above the level of the primitive is to gain survival advantage. However, whenever one's behavior is geared solely to position them above another, it smacks of the AB influence, even when that positioning hinges on *denying* the AB influence ("Look at me, I am better and smarter than you because I am more sensitive, more ethical, more religious, more spiritual, more altruistic, etc..."). Any behavior with the sole purpose of one-upping is automatic brain driven.

Another interesting pattern arises among many wealthy individuals who are staunch advocates of those with less than them. Our automatic brains have had the better part of 200,000 years to recognize danger. Wealth, when viewed solely from the neurons of the automatic brain, is synonymous with power. And those who are powerful face Schaden

Freude (see chapter 12) by those who have less wealth, who are less powerful. Hence, the automatic brain picks up potential danger from this
exposure. There are two ways the AB reacts to this danger—fight or flight.
The fight would be for the wealthy to flaunt their power and use it to sub-
jugate; the flight would be to join hands with them—to make them feel as
though the wealthy are on their side. If you, the wealthy, are viewed as on
the same team as the poor than your automatic brain feels secure that the
latter will not want to take you down ("We're just like you. We're on your
side. It's the other rich guys whom you have to fear"). I see this played out
in the political arena, as well as many public displays of altruism. Either
way, the automatic brain is responsible for the choices, and authentic
progress is never made.

How do we make choices using the power of our mind rather than
the AB? How do we recognize if our decisions and choices are dominated
by the AB? Maria, a 29-year-old, single, professional woman, recently
came to my office to discuss her difficulty with relationships. Maria had
been involved with a man named Christopher for three years. The relationship was volatile, and at times verbally and almost physically abusive.
Yet Maria was unable to leave him. Every time she tried, she would be
dragged right back into the relationship (yes, just like Michael Corleone).
During a particularly volatile period, Maria met another man, Greg. On
paper, Greg sounds terrific. He is the antithesis of Christopher: financially
secure in his own job, more stable emotionally, adored by Maria's family,
and a loyal son to his. The fact that Maria came into my office so confused
tipped me off that her AB was calling the shots. To get more of a handle on
her thoughts, I suggested we fill in a Revelation Grid.

When you're developing a Revelation Grid, the first challenge is to
identify the danger perceived by the AB. I assured Maria that her situation
is not uncommon. Clearly, one of her main danger triggers was *not* having
a boyfriend.

Her grid looked like this:

Circumstance/Trigger	Danger	Comfort/Safety
Having a boyfriend	*Commitment; lack of independence; may be the wrong guy.*	Emotional safety net; not having to meet someone; make family happy.
Not having a boyfriend	Clock is ticking; family driving me crazy: "What's wrong with you?" lack of security; not fulfilling family wishes (i.e., of getting married and giving them grandchildren).	*Getting to know myself; more independent; free; think for myself; figure out what I really want.*

After discussing this with Maria, it seemed obvious that a mindful decision at this moment in her life would be not to have a boyfriend. Her AB thoughts in boxes 2 and 3 clearly had influenced much of her behavior as far back as her early teens. I pointed out to Maria that her automatic brain appeared to be looking out for her by trying to get her what she wanted out of life—a committed relationship with a man she loves and respects as much as he loves and respects her. But the manipulation, seduction, and lies of the AB were, in fact, preventing her from getting what she truly desires. When she makes the decision to have a boyfriend, it does not feel right, so she lets him go. Then the automatic brain (box 3) kicks in and bounces her right back to box 2, all in the name of protecting her from danger. No wonder she is confused!

After our meeting, Maria felt strong as she made her own decision to put a hold on dating, at least for a while, while she looked for other ways to connect with her mind. She had broken with Christopher before this, and now she would make a clean break with Greg.

Everything was going well for about a month, until Maria saw Greg talking with another woman in an intimate manner. Because of the stress she felt, she made an appointment to see me. She believed that when she saw Greg with another woman she now realized how much she loved him and wanted to be with him. I knew Maria's automatic brain was on full alert. I decided to fill out a new Revelation Grid, with the danger trigger being, *Not having a relationship with Greg*. This is what we came up with:

Circumstance/Trigger	Danger	Comfort/Safety
Relationship with Greg	*Constricted; less independent; sacrificing growth; giving into traditional, close-minded expectations.*	Make families happy; feeling trust and security; not being single, moving toward long-term relationship; financial security; security blanket.
Not having relationship with Greg	Scared of him being with someone else; not satisfying checklist of needs and wants in a mate; make family angry; no relationship at 29; have to start all over.	

Maria was now so sure that Greg was Mr. Right that she could not come up with any thoughts for box 4. This helps us see the power of the manipulation, seduction, and lies of the AB. If Maria follows this path, she is likely to end up with a scenario that is fraught with difficulties. The thoughts in her first box 4 have not disappeared in a month's time. The automatic brain has simply buried them for the sole false purpose of protecting her.

How can Maria stick with her mindful decision, relying on it rather than the seduction of the AB? The first step is a commitment to believe, trust, and take direction from her mind rather than from the automatic brain. It is a major leap to evaluate all the thoughts in boxes 2 and 3 and not believe them at all. It is important to realize that when others' needs and values creep into your automatic brain boxes, it is their ABs and need to protect themselves that is influencing your thoughts. Playing to the AB can only lead to stagnation.

Everything for Maria and Greg may be fine for a time, until Greg develops a bleeding hemorrhoid, infected pimple on his butt, or wants his mother to accompany them on a vacation trip! I heard Steve Harvey, comedian, author, and syndicated talk-show host, respond to a listener, "Your girlfriend never looks so good until on the arm of another man." Greg never looked so good until Maria saw him chatting it up with another woman. Decisions made this way are AB-based and lead to unfulfilling results.

For assertively dealing with her "old-school" parents, I told Maria to tell them how much she loves and respects them, and that if they love her, they must ease up their control. That's hard because the automatic brain, as we saw in Chapter 7, has a love receptor that inhibits its activity. When that receptor is vacant, it causes the automatic brain to fire. The threat that her parents might withhold their love if she didn't have a man in her life sends a strong danger message to get a man before it is too late. She is not denying that she is getting older. But she must also not deny that she wants to get to know herself, become more independent, be free, think for herself, and figure out what she really wants. For these are her mindful desires, and making decisions based on these yields results that keep on coming and are self-perpetuating. They attract into our lives what is right for us.

One of the areas that presents great confusion when trying to decipher mindful decision making vs. AB-based is physical attraction. Physical attraction, when synergistic and not opportunistic, is mindful within our physical world. Certainly, many factors influence wanting to look good. In any case, a feeling of attractiveness is a powerful tool to overcome the automatic brain and begin to connect with the mind. Actually, our appearance can be a physical manifestation of the power of our mind.

You don't have to turn to plastic surgery for this. A healthy lifestyle, and healthy thoughts, can lead to attractiveness. No matter what you think you look like, the next time you go out with a group of people, do not look in the mirror all night to see how you look. Do not wonder what people are thinking about you. I'm not denying that people are having thoughts about you…because they are! Instead, throughout the evening, repeat in your mind, "I am strong, I stand tall, I am powerful, I am smiling, I am attractive…I am strong, I stand tall, I am powerful, I am smiling, I am attractive." Next time you see me walking up the aisle of a sold-out movie theater, carrying a bucket of popcorn, read my mind, because that's what I am uttering as the entire audience stares down at me. As you utter these words, you actually do stand more upright, do appear more confident, do feel better about yourself, and you do become more attractive, all without thinking about it. You just are; you just become.

When you look at a dolphin, what do you feel? Doesn't looking at a dolphin have a way of making you feel good? I bet it is the trusty smile implanted on a dolphin's face. The smile is attracting. A simple smile on your face may have the same effect – try it.

Learning how to make mindful decisions helps diminish the influence of the AB. Anytime you're on an airline trip, the flight attendant will instruct passengers that in case of decreased pressure they should place an oxygen mask over their own face before placing one on a child; for if they did not have oxygen, they would not be in a position to help the child.

Parents of small children may find it hard to relax into a dispassionate response; the overprotective-parent nature of the AB might lead them to think they must put the mask on their child first, or sacrifice the parent-child relationship for the sake of the children. The decision to put themselves and their relationship first is mindful. Making such decisions allows you to contribute authentically: personally, professionally, and globally.

Seeing the influence of our mind within the realities of our physical world can be validating. Once we learn not to believe, trust, or take direction from our AB through mindful decision-making, we stop brain drain. Being assertive, passionate, and demonstrating willpower is the evidence of your success. This is the place where we can continue to grow, create, and shape our destiny.

CHAPTER FIFTEEN

In the Eye of the Beholder

❧✦❧

"Focusing on the act of breathing clears the mind
of all daily distractions and clears our energy
enabling us to better connect with the Spirit within."

–Author Unknown

The automatic brain is continually running with its danger antennae raised. As I explained in earlier chapters, the automatic brain is controlled symbolically by an on/off switch. If external circumstances or internal thoughts signal danger, the switch is flipped on. Once the switch is flipped the fight-or-flight reaction begins as the AB does whatever it takes by all means necessary to set us up to fight or flee danger. By all means necessary means the creation of a powerful, recognizable response and the fabrication of all sorts of very strong, influential thoughts that simply are the amalgamation of stored memories. The actions of the AB to "protect" us leads to the response that we have labeled stress.

Many people have shared with me, and I have experienced myself, the sense of being overwhelmed. This swirling, powerful feeling of no-way-out is the foundation of stress, and the result of believing, trusting, and taking direction from our automatic brain, which—through manipulation, seduction, and lies—has fooled us into believing that the thoughts it generates will protect us. The feeling of being overwhelmed is the turbulent waters, I spoke about earlier, that leak through the small hole in the dike, only to expand the hole, flooding our trust in the power of our mind. The "flooding" trust in our automatic brain results in the certainty that to believe in the power of the mind is a pipe dream or unrealistic nonsense. To prevent the overwhelm hinges on us keeping the dike plugged with our finger, not allowing the automatic brain to drain into the garden of our mind. This and this alone will stop the whirlwind and relieve the stress.

A Revelation Grid can help you see more clearly the thoughts that drive the sense of being overwhelmed and feeling stuck. Obviously, you can't whip up a Revelation Grid in the heat of battle every time the fight-or-flight response is triggered. Instead, it's enough to become aware of the physiological feelings produced by stress, as that will let you engage your mind's power, even if you don't quite understand yet what that is.

Stress is a generalized physiological response to perceived danger. Dangers vary greatly, but the reaction is the same. During my practice of over 20 years, many of my patients have felt paralyzed by stress; the signals of danger are real and easy to see. Devastating life events like illness, death of a spouse, or illness or death of a child, trigger the automatic brain causing the sensation of stress. And who would be so cold and emotionless not to feel this and be directed by it? With the uncertainty of the current economy, job security is precarious. Should not we believe, trust, and take direction from our automatic brain's response to this clear and present danger?

However, it doesn't take a world-shaking event to fire the automatic brain. As we saw in the earlier chapters, throughout life our AB calls up danger memories formed during childhood and uses them as a warning of danger. Going out in public, or negotiating a deal on a new car, as examples, may cause as much of a fight-or-flight response as losing a spouse for some people. For others, public speaking may be as brutally painful as the illness of a child. I am certainly not minimizing the stress of those facing serious trauma; nevertheless, the automatic brain does not discriminate. Just as the person who lost a spouse may have fleeting moments of peace and happiness, so too does the person facing public speaking until his AB reminds him that he should be afraid. Many have asked me how one recognizes what is an automatic brain thought and what is coming from our mind. The answer is simple: any negative or upsetting thought that pops into your head when you are relaxed, having fun, enjoying the moment, first awakening, or succeeding at something arises from the automatic brain—its attempt to help you flee or fight these "dangers."

Naturally, as a physician for many years I have encountered many people battling cancer. Some share with me the phenomenon of enjoying fellowship moments with family and friends, laughing, talking, and generally forgetting that they have cancer—until their automatic brain reminds them to be prepared and on guard at all times. They then slip back to believing, trusting, and taking direction from this automatic brain, for "survival" purposes, of course. The happiness and joy ends and they get back on the cancer train. Another temporary respite comes when they awaken in the morning—they experience a window of a few seconds to a couple of minutes before the protective veil of the AB returns. As they bask in the calm of these moments, an alert of vulnerability automatically puts them on notice to "remember" why they should feel unease and stress. If you have recently lost your job or face an upcoming challenge, when you first awaken, how long does it take your automatic brain to remind you that you should be on guard?

The reality is that the automatic brain goes into protective fight-or-flight mode when *any* event it perceives as negative occurs. The perception of negativity and fear implies a threat to our survival, whether related to our own mortality or indirectly through someone else's negative experience. The AB's unshakable need to protect us shapes the choices we make at these times, yielding decisions aimed at satisfying this need. In short, the choices we make during these hard times are not mindful but based on the direction of our automatic brain. The strong and compelling nature of the AB uses the immediacy of the real situation as a barrier to block our access to our mind. It is the single greatest barrier to the richest source of solutions to any challenge. The firm block of the AB is self-validating representing further "proof" that its physical response is the only way to protect and save us.

At the risk of belaboring the point, I want to emphasize that the fight-or-flight reaction causes stress, and its only function is to ensure our survival. Thoughts and behaviors stemming from this mechanism shape the way we think and act during these times. Those responses don't address the circumstances of the moment, but link to danger memories (i.e. from the past) and to thoughts about the future as they try—unfortunately, with fraud and lies—to protect us from pain and suffering, and to keep us alive.

When my wife was diagnosed with breast cancer, my inner guidance (which I accessed with meditation) told me, "Everything that matters is right here, now, in the moment, in the present." When we awaken in the morning, for a few brief seconds we are in the moment. There is no danger in the moment. The danger comes when the automatic brain reviews danger memories and projects into the future, to remind us we should be on guard, on the lookout.

I can hear the skeptics now: "What happens when real danger is present?" Living your life continually preparing for danger actually makes you *less* prepared. That is why the cautionary warnings of the automatic brain can't be trusted. Making decisions while overwhelmed leads to poor judgment. To be sure, at the moment you need the physical response of the automatic brain, it will be there, as solid as ever.

Among the first physical reactions, when the AB is triggered, is rapid breathing. Most of the time it's not apparent, but as I explained in Chapter 2, the fight-or-flight reaction preps the body to do just that—fight or flee. And that signals the lungs to breathe faster and less deeply to boost oxygen delivery to the body. Just as you should not believe or trust the thoughts generated at these times, so too the physiological response is counterproductive. The shallow, rapid breaths serve well when fighting or fleeing a predator, but as a response to everyday "dangers", the generic and primitive nature of the automatic brain response is disproportionate.

Controlling the automatic process of breathing during the fight-or-flight response is a key step in transitioning from AB-based decisions to mindful ones. Bringing the scattered, confused automatic brain back to the present moment by mindfully directing your focus on your breathing is an effective way to curb the fight-or-flight response and eventually shut it off.

Breathing was a central element of my karate training. In fact, all relaxation methods from time immemorial have involved breathing control as central to their practice. Even smoking, a notably destructive practice, illustrates the point: Smokers use their breathing/puffing as an attempt to relax. Smokers grab a cigarette during times of stress. As they light up the cigarette, they take a long, slow drag deeply into their lungs, hold for a moment, and then exhale. The only thing that exists at that moment is the act of inhaling and exhaling. Of course, the problem in this example is that the individual is breathing entirely through the mouth and inhaling toxins. Nevertheless, the smoker does experience a measure of relaxation by this act. It is my belief that, beyond the effects of nicotine, cigarette smokers are in some respects addicted to this ritualistic breathing exercise.

When the AB senses danger, the switch flips on and the fight-or-flight reaction begins. Below are some of the signs of the fight or flight, hence signaling that you are stressed:

- Moodiness (fight or flight)
- Agitation (fight or flight)
- Restlessness (flight)
- Short temper (fight)
- Irritability, impatience (fight)

- Inability to relax (flight)
- Feeling tense and "on edge" (flight)
- Feeling overwhelmed (fight or flight)
- Sense of loneliness and isolation (flight)
- Depression or general unhappiness (flight)
- Memory problems (fight or flight)
- Indecisiveness (fight or flight)
- Inability to concentrate (fight of flight)
- Trouble thinking clearly (fight or flight)
- Poor judgment (fight or flight)
- Seeing only the negative (flight)
- Anxious or racing thoughts (flight)
- Constant worrying (flight)
- Loss of objectivity (fight)
- Fearful anticipation (fight or flight)
- Eating more or less (fight or flight)
- Sleeping too much or too little (fight or flight)
- Isolating yourself from others (flight)
- Procrastination, neglecting responsibilities (flight)
- Using alcohol, cigarettes, or drugs to relax (fight or flight)
- Nervous habits (e.g., nail biting, pacing) (fight or flight)
- Teeth grinding or jaw clenching (fight or flight)
- Overdoing activities (e.g., exercising, shopping) (fight or flight)
- Overreacting to unexpected problems (fight)
- Picking fights with others (fight)

Mindful breathing is slow, steady, and deep (as opposed to the breathing of the AB, which is rapid and shallow). You can do it without being noticed, in public and around people. Initially, though, I suggest practicing it in privacy. Breathe through your nose and out through either your mouth or nose. For the purpose of establishing the right habit, I suggest breathing out through your mouth, at first. Here's a step-by-step suggestion of this procedure:

- Sit in a comfortable chair in a quiet room.
- Gently close your eyes.
- Push out your abdomen. This will draw air in by engaging the diaphragm muscles.
- As you draw air in, be conscious not to sniff. The breath should come from the back of your throat and sound grumbling, almost like a snore.
- If that's too difficult at first, instead start by drawing in the air through your nose. The steadiness of your breathing is more important than whether you draw in from the back of your throat.
- As your abdomen expands, follow it by the expansion of the sides of your chest.
- Picture in your mind the air moving in through your nose, through your windpipe (trachea), and into the outer reaches of your lungs. Picture your chest expanding, and more importantly, your upper back filling out completely, as though it is a balloon being inflated to its maximum potential.
- When you reach the peak of each breath, let your lungs deflate naturally, but control your breath as it leaves through your mouth. Let the air move slowly as though the balloon has sprung a small leak. Listen to it as it makes a gentle wind sound. The exhaling should take at least twice as long as the inhaling. The more air you expel, the more your lungs will automatically refill. The more void you leave in your lungs by exhaling, the more space that you can fill with clean, fresh, crisp, life-giving air. In a sense, as you learn to control the automatic brain by emptying it, you make more room to expand your mind.

One thing you may notice when you try this exercise. You may feel as though you can't finish your breath, as though it stops short before it feels deep and satisfying. I suggest that as you take this breath, you picture in your mind your bright smiling face. You may have a photo of this. Ion my computer desktop I have a photo of my wife and I with big bright smiles. As I take in my deep breath, I make sure this is the image I see in my mind. For you must understand, this breathing is contrary to the programming of the automatic brain, which is fast and shallow in order to help your fight or flee. This slow, deep breathing is enough to trigger the AB. The image of your smiling face interrupts this effect and essentially slows or plugs the brain drain.

Once you have mastered this technique, you can use it in front of people without their being aware. Of course, your eyes will not close and your inspiration and expiration may not be so long and loud; nonetheless, you will be able to suck in deep relaxing breaths and release longer cleansing breaths.

I often use this tactic when I have to deal with my children's bickering. When they were younger, they recall me saying, "Daddy's going to take a time out." To control the automatic brain, the reactive anger (my fight) I may have felt toward their fighting, I would depart for a minute or two to another room and focus on my breathing. When I returned, I was in a much better frame of mind to deal with my kids.

Breathing must be the initial focus in controlling brain drain. I view our mind as the portal to the divine nature in all of us, and meditation is the vehicle. Through this effort to connect with our mind, I believe we gain a sense of peace and a feeling that we actually can create our future and attain our true desires. This is the place where the law of attraction is the dominant rule.

If you've never meditated, trying to do it twice a day is unreasonable. Even for those who have mastered it, daily meditation may not be practical. Not to start the process at all, though, is like being given the answer to your greatest problem and rejecting it. I have experienced it myself, and I've talked to many others who have themselves experienced the benefits of meditation.

When you relax into meditation, the automatic brain goes into overdrive and conjures up many blocking thoughts to prevent it. Why would it act this way? Because the act of relaxation and meditation leaves you vulnerable to attack. The AB doesn't care that the likelihood of being attacked while meditating is negligible. It is binary – on or off, black or white. The AB simply reverts to the primitive survival patterns. We need to recognize, though, that the distracting thoughts that creep into our brain as we relax into meditation are irrelevant and fraudulent. Do not engage them by stringing thoughts together.

For example, if you face a busy day at work—deadlines, presentations, paperwork, phone calls, bills due—your brain is likely to resist meditation as the worst possible way to prepare for the coming battles. But persist; meditate. As you carve out, say, ten minutes, do not fight the contrary thoughts as they come into your mind. Acknowledge that your AB is trying to protect you (falsely) and realize that you have evolved normally as a thinking human. That is, your brain is working the way it was programmed. Whatever the thoughts may be, and as crazy as they may seem (and I mean certifiably crazy), does not matter. What matters is that you should not be ambushed by the automatic brain, which will do whatever it takes to prevent you from getting into the 'vulnerable' position of meditation.

This, of course, hinges on belief. When the thoughts start coming, it is essential for you not to believe them at all. Not even a slight amount. Since once you believe, for instance, that you must take care of an item on your to-do list right away, the more you try to stop the thoughts the more they will come, all related to that list and more lists and whatever seemingly crazy association with any item on your list that may have nothing to do with anything. When you decide to take the time to meditate, you must believe in this activity 100 percent. If you have doubt that you should be taking time doing it, you are removing the finger from the dike and eventually your mind will be flooded with the turbulence of the AB, sabotaging your efforts to connect with your mind, and realize its innate power.

So how do you get there? Find a quiet room with the lights low or off. If possible, kneel on the floor, resting on your calves with your heels touching your butt, hands on thighs tilted slightly inward, sitting up high. If this position is more than you want to tackle for now, a comfortable chair will suffice. Close your eyes. Begin taking slow, deep breaths in through your nose and out through your mouth as described earlier. Direct your mind's eye on the flow of air in and out. The only thing that exists is your breath. You are present, in the moment.

As you breathe, visualize every atom of stressful waste products washing away with your exhaled breath. After several cycles, begin contracting individual muscle groups with inhalation and relaxing them as you exhale. Start with your toes, then calves, then thighs, then butt, then low back, etc..., finishing with your scalp muscles. Once this is finished, visualize yourself walking into an elevator. See the elevator doors close and with each inhale/exhale cycle, watch the floor indicator go further down into the sub-basements.

Go down about 10 levels. When you reach the tenth sublevel, watch the doors open. What do you see? This is your place of serenity—this is the garden of your mind. Imagine yourself talking to yourself there or to whoever or whatever greets you. Agree that together you can face any situation with calm energy. After a few moments, say goodbye but believe that the power of your mind will be with you during all moments, not just during meditation.

Get back in the elevator and go slowly up. Continue the inhale/exhale cycles, the latter longer than the former. When you get off the elevator, continue a few more cycles and then gently open your eyes.

During meditation, it is important to see yourself as the person you want to be. Everything that happens during meditation is in the present moment. Your brain may wander into the past or future, but do not be mistaken—this wandering is the normal behavior of your protective AB. Even in the domain of your mind, it may appear. Just do not believe, trust, or take direction from it.

Your own meditation does not necessarily have to take this form. The essential components, though, of any type of meditation are control of breathing, focus, visualization, and being in the moment. Within these criteria, many variations can serve as meditative practices. Exercise, for example, is an activity that lends itself to meditation. Some of my greatest inspiration has come during a run. I no longer run marathons, but I recall that during training, when I was at the end of a long run and approached a hill I needed to climb, I would get a twinge of nervousness (my AB was alive). My strategy was to focus on the path in front of me, every step. That would guide me up the hill despite the warning signals from my automatic brain. Even as I run much shorter distances today, toward the end, when I see how much farther I have to run, I tend to get breathless. But when I focus on the path directly in front of me, my endurance seems endless—the end actually exists in each step.

To elaborate the concept of creating a future by visualizing in the moment, I turn to a tennis player who competed in the 2007 US Open. Before each serve, she closed her eyes briefly. Asked later what she was doing, she replied, "I was visualizing an ace." Not all players close their eyes, but you can be certain that the most successful players as they toss the ball are seeing an ace, at that moment, before it happens.

The goal of a service ace is not the only place for visualization. Martial artists see their hand passing through a brick as they are punching. As they kick, they see the other side. The moment predicts the future and is the future. These are examples of moving meditation and examples of the mind moving unobstructed by the automatic brain. For as soon as the automatic brain shows itself, so does doubt.

Creating authentic results in the language of the automatic brain is the manifestation of our mind and begins the process that allows you to believe, trust, and take direction from your true nature. The language of the automatic brain appears in the areas of money (which can secure food, clothing, and shelter for our survival), health (which can threaten our survival), and relationships (without love we can wither and die). When we create things with the power of our mind, they become manifest in these areas. Many people try to visualize exact things that they feel they need and want. For example, if they think an appearance on Oprah will bring them the greatest success, they may put a picture on the wall alongside Oprah. Or they may visualize themselves in a big house, or driving a big car, or walking down the aisle with a trophy wife. All or none of the above may be what is right for you. But it is impossible for anyone of us to know exactly what is right for us. To believe, trust, and take direction from the power of our mind, we must understand that what is right for us will come to us. It will appear in the three areas above. In what form or shape or in what time frame though is not certain. But to make it happen, you must believe 100 percent (not 25 or 50 or 75 or 99.99 percent) that you will always find a way and a way will always find you.

A story I first read many years ago told by Joe Hyams in *Zen in the Martial Arts* illustrates the importance of mastering the moment to create a desirable future. I'll paraphrase:

A 10-year-old boy wants to learn karate. He goes to a popular sensei (karate master) at a nearby dojo (school) and asks, "Sensei, how long will it take me to get my black belt?"

The Sensei replies, "Ten years, my son."

Quizzically, the boy responds, "Ten years? If I train day and night, seven days a week, how long, then, will it take me?"

The Sensei looks into the boy's eyes and replies, "Twenty years."

Confused, the boy responds, "Even if I come to live in the *dojo*, make it my home, and train side by side with you and all the top instructors? How long, then, will it take?"

Now the Sensei looks deep into the boy's eyes and says, "Thirty years."

Disappointed and perplexed, the boy admits, "I don't understand."

The Sensei explains: "You see, my son, if you have one eye on your goal, you have only one eye on the path in which to find the way."

Always having one eye on our future reveals the pesky and distracting nature of the AB; hence, its nature to sabotage the mind's ability to attract into our lives everything that is right for us. When we focus on the present, we position ourselves to attract the future that will be right for us. That is not to say that having a goal is not important, but simply that looking up that hill, as I did during marathon training, literally took my breath away. As I focused on my individual steps, I achieved success. When I began the process of writing this book, the idea of being where I am today, seemed mind-boggling. Focusing on writing in the moment created the goal. This is how we begin to understand how our mind works.

The moments that exist during your meditation help you realize that your moments are a more accurate gauge of your future than any fear-induced automatic brain planning. Allowing your future to merge with the present creates your desired goal. Breathe, meditate, visualize, and understand that moments well-lived add up to a future of your dreams.

CHAPTER SIXTEEN

A Healthy Mind

*"A sound mind in a sound body is a short but full description
of a happy state in this world".*

–John Locke

How do you feel when you wake up in the morning? Do you ever feel grumpy? How do you feel if you go without food for a whole day? Do you ever feel lightheaded if you don't drink enough water?

In order to understand your automatic brain, you must make sure that your mind and body are in a condition to manage stress. This is a very important concept, and one that too many people ignore. Not too long ago a woman approached me because she had heard that I was interested in the mind-body connection and an integrated approach toward my patients. She expressed an interest in fields of energy medicine as well as meditation and other forms of alternative medicine.

I try not to judge others, as that would feed my automatic brain. However, my professional diagnosis was that she was morbidly obese. Although she seemed aware of the influence the mind has on the body, she was demonstrably unaware of the effect her own automatic brain had on her body. Some may disagree with me on this, and claim that obesity is more nature (in the genes) than nurture (a result of psychosocial factors). Nonetheless, eating at levels higher than necessary for sustenance (i.e., what you need to survive) indicates that the automatic brain is driving your behavior. That is not to say that morbid obesity is the only face of the automatic brain. On the contrary, it is just the most visible. (Since the automatic brain drives us all to some extent, we should resist judging others. See chapter 12.)

Your automatic brain may have you think, "If only I take that vitamin, follow that diet, or do that exercise, I will be happy, healthy, and fit." The mind does not have such strict rules. The only constant of the mind is that by following it, rather than the automatic brain, allows you to live a genuinely fulfilling life. Eating, exercise, sleep, and supplementation play a role in achieving this goal—but only to make realizing the power of the mind much easier.

Nutrition

In order to maintain a clear mind, proper nutrition is essential. Have you ever felt hypoglycemic (the result of a low blood sugar)? I'm not asking if you're a diabetic. When our blood sugar goes down, we can feel irritable and short-tempered, and have trouble concentrating. This illustrates why our physical state must be at its peak in order for us to calm our AB. Calming the automatic brain requires that the section of the neocortex where the mind resides remains in balance. When our blood sugar fluctuates, it stimulates our automatic brain to react in fight-or-flight mode. When sugar gets low, the body releases adrenaline and cortisol (fight mode); when sugar is too high, the body goes into flight mode, trying desperately to remove sugar from the circulation and shift it into the muscles, to be burned later as fuel, or turned to fat for storage.

Feeding the AB means feeding it with sugar and fat. I discussed this in Chapter 12. You need a clear, balanced mind to utilize its power. And the key to that requires maintaining blood sugar within a healthful range. I am not advocating a low carbohydrate or Atkins-like diet. The fact is brain cells require sugar. In fact, sugar is the only substance that brain cells can use for energy. It's just that the automatic brain creates an exaggerated requirement for sugar (just as it over exaggerates everything).

When you feel a craving for sugar, know that your automatic brain is controlling—and distorting—this urge.

Willpower and self-control are behaviors I associate with the mind. Nowhere in our lives does self-control play a clearer role than in our eating habits. Since we need food to survive, you might expect that the need to eat is an automatic one, not requiring thought. So, too, we might expect that to cease eating once a sustenance level of food has been consumed would also be automatic. Ah, would that be convenient if it were so. The problem arises when we begin eating above sustenance—above what we need to survive.

Okinawans, among the longest-living people in the world, have a phrase, Hara hachi bu, to describe their cultural habit of stopping eating when they are 80 percent full. This fits within the framework of the automatic brain: For the brain to get the message that the stomach is full generally takes about 12 minutes. The automatic brain likely evolved this phenomenon to make sure that we have a few extra calories as a safety margin. In other words, the automatic brain overstates what we need for survival. Perhaps 10,000 years ago we needed the safety margin. Today, eating too much is obsolete.

If you stop eating at a point just shy of feeling satiated, about 12 minutes (give or take) after that point, you will be full. Think about how many bites or forkfuls of foods would otherwise go down during those 12 minutes. Not only would it be in excess of what you and your brain really need, but your blood sugar is likely to rise above a healthful level, stimulating the automatic brain to store the excess for later conversion to energy.

There is much to say about what foods we should be eating. For the purposes of my book, though, and for the purpose of authentic growth, I am less interested in *what* you eat than *how much* you eat. One of the findings of the experiments during Biosphere II, whose participants experienced unintended caloric reduction, was a strengthened link between calorie reduction and slower aging. In other words, if you eat less, you could age more slowly. The automatic brain, though, would have you believe that the more you eat, the more cushion you will have for future famines—i.e., the safety margin. But increasingly, research is proving that a diet of eating less actually leads to a longer and healthier life. It's yet another example of the manipulation, seduction, and lies our AB invents to keep us out of "danger."

Many people insist to me that they really do not eat much. The definition of "much," of course, is relative. A majority of Americans do overeat, so comparing yourself to your family and friends may make you think you don't eat too much. But the comparison is from the automatic brain and not your mind. Your mind knows what is true and what is not. And the truth is that most of us are eating too much.

Your AB tries to "protect" all aspects of you. The idea that you are the way you are because you need to foster self-control is a hard pill to swallow and can lead to a negative opinion of yourself. But your automatic brain rejects these negative opinions, because those opinions could imply vulnerability and, as we have seen with the overly dramatic AB, the threat of death. Your AB will deceive you as much as you let it. Therefore, it will cause you to look for blame in things that are out of your control so not to demean your sense of self. For instance, I'm the way I am because it's in my genes, or because I have a hormonal problem, or because I am big boned. These are the flight reactions to the danger trigger of lacking self-control, of being weak.

I define self-control and willpower as a person's ability to control the automatic brain. That is what we have come to recognize as the self. Mastering self-control over our eating is a great place to begin. It can start by eating until you are 80 percent full. The only self-control you need is during those 12 minutes it takes your brain to realize it is full. As you focus on the amount you eat, you develop confidence in choosing what to eat. Once you master self-control, you can break the power of the automatic brain to drive you to eat more sugar and fat. You will gain a clearer idea about how much and what types of sugar and fat you should be eating.

One strategy is to add healthy foods to your diet instead of eliminating the unhealthy. Unknowingly, you will become 80 percent full on the healthy foods. Here are some examples of foods to add to whatever you are used to eating.

Fiber—Both types of fiber, insoluble and soluble are excellent to add into your diet. Insoluble fiber provides volume to food without adding a lot of calories. Foods rich in insoluble fiber include high fiber cereal, whole wheat bread, wheat bran, fruits and vegetables. Soluble fiber helps stabilize your blood sugar levels, which in turn can better control hunger and cravings. Also, this type of fiber slows down the transit time of food in your gut, so it may keep you fuller for longer. Foods rich in soluble fiber include strawberries, apples, pears, oatmeal, chickpeas, and beans.

Foods with High Water Content—fruits and veggies with a high water content helps to fill you up, so you'll eat less. Examples of these are watermelon, lettuce, tomatoes, cucumber, mushrooms, grapefruit, and cantaloupe.

Lean Protein—include some type of lean protein with every meal. Good sources include chicken breast, canned light tuna, wild salmon (fresh and canned), egg whites, crab, shrimp, tilapia, turkey breast, tofu, lean red meat, low-fat dairy, beans and lentils.

Foods That Take Work to Eat— People eat less of the very same foods when they require a bit of work. For example, shelled peanuts versus unshelled peanuts and prepare soybeans in the pod versus the straight bean.

Warm Beverages—sipping a hot, low-cal beverage is a great way to stave off extra calories when you're looking to eat out of pure boredom. And because they're hot, you'll have to sip slowly over an extended period of time. Choose beverages under 100-calories such as green and herbal teas, diet hot cocoa, skim latte and cappuccino, and reduced sodium bouillon. Since most green tea comes from China, it is imperative that you choose only organic brands. My favorite is the Yogi brand.

Spicy Food and Capsaicin—many people report feeling satisfied with less food when the meal is spicy hot. Plus, you automatically eat slower and drink more water! If your taste buds can handle the heat, add chili peppers, hot sauce and salsa to your meals.

Supplements

No magical supplements exist that allows you to believe, trust, and take direction from the power of the mind. My practice is called The NY Center for Longevity & Wellness, and many come to me for the silver bullet to assure both longevity and wellness. What they will find after reading this book and meeting with me is that the best way to live long, well, and happy is to stop brain drain and acknowledge the power of our mind.

That said there are supplements that can help with neurotransmission; that is, help with the way nerves talk to each other. And as with diet, the lack of certain nutrients may make it more likely for the automatic brain to function unrestrained.

There are hundreds of supplements, and hundreds of opinions as to the best supplements for brain function. I'll suggest a few I feel are most important for staying focused and bolstering the mind and calming the AB. The most important is a form of fish oil, an omega-3 fatty acid. Although the mention of fat may prompt concerns of heart disease and obesity, fat comprises about 60 percent of the brain and nerves. Though the body cannot manufacture omega-3 fatty acids, they are essential to human health. So omega-3 fatty acids must be obtained from food or from supplements. Omega-3 fatty acids can be found in fish, such as salmon, tuna, and halibut; other marine life such as algae and krill; certain plants (including purslane); and nut oils. Also known as polyunsaturated fatty acids (PUFAs), omega-3 fatty acids play a crucial role in brain function as well as overall growth and development.

DHA, or docosahexaenoic acid, is the primary structural component of brain tissue and is an omega-3 fatty acid. In general, the colder the water that fish inhabit, the higher the content of omega-3 in their fish oil. Good sources of DHA include salmon, sardines, and tuna. Eggs have a small amount of DHA in them, but the most healthful source of dietary DHA is seafood. Two 4-ounce servings of omega-3-rich fish per week should give you adequate omega-3 fatty acids, especially DHA. Besides fish oils, vegetable oils (primarily flaxseed, soy, and canola) are also rich sources of omega-3 fatty acids. Fish and flax are among the top brain-building foods, especially for growing children.

Omega-3 supplements are available everywhere. Most are a combination of eicosapentaenoic acid (EPA) and DHA. EPA is important mostly for its anti-inflammatory and cardiovascular benefits; DHA for its nervous system benefits, including for the retina. Many brands list a total of 1000 milligrams of omega-3 per capsule (and the capsules tend to be large), but have less than 50 percent of my recommended amounts of EPA and DHA. You need to be sure the brand uses a microfiltration system to eliminate heavy metals. I suggest taking 600mg to 1200 mg of DHA daily. This may be difficult to get in a supplement pill, so diet is an important source, including liquid oils.

Generally speaking, a broad-spectrum, high quality multivitamin/nutritional supplement can contribute to enhanced nerve-system function and brain circulation. These supplements have the proper blend of antioxidants (the brain is one of the organs most sensitive to what scientists call oxidative stress, essentially internal rusting). The most common antioxidants are vitamin A (the carotenoid group), vitamin C, vitamin E, and selenium. Glutathione is the most abundant naturally occurring antioxidant in the human body. Our body synthesizes it from three amino acids (the building blocks of protein). Cysteine is the amino acid most difficult for the body to manufacture, so it is important that our intake of cysteine be adequate. A good supplement usually contains cysteine in the form of n-acetylcysteine (NAC).

Next, a supplement should be high in B vitamins, especially B6, B9 (folic acid), and B12. All are crucial for nerve cell function. You can ask your doctor about a high-dose, prescription-strength derivative of folic acid that research has shown to be effective as a replacement for, or addition to, prescription anti-depressants. If you are taking anti-depressants or your physician has recommended that you do, you may ask to try this as a natural alternative. Some supplements contain two nutrients that also aid in maintaining a healthy nervous system and may boost energy levels—alpha lipoic acid and l-carnitine (or acetyl-l-carnitine), respectively. The amount of those substances in a multivitamin is not enough for the nerve and energy benefits. You have to take them separately for the best results. I suggest taking 200mg – 600mg of alpha lipoic acid and 500mg – 1000mg of l-Carnitine.

As we age physiologically, hormones fluctuate and decrease. This is especially noticeable during perimenopause and menopause for women. The physiological symptoms can significantly interfere with mood and optimism. That's why I feel this is an important part of the mind-body-spirit connection. Supplementing with the proper doses of estrogen, progesterone, testosterone, and DHEA, among others, may help. This takes the expertise of a doctor who is knowledgeable in the area of bio-identical hormones.

Exercise

Several recent studies have shown that exercise helps prevent dementia and sharpen cognitive function in aging adults. It's actually more effective than medication, vitamins, or such mental exercises as doing crossword puzzles.

The pituitary and hypothalamus (integral parts of the automatic brain) produce proteins known as endorphins during strenuous exercise, excitement, and orgasm. Endorphins play a dual role—they sharpen many of our senses, thus aiding in the fight-or-flight of survival, and they mask pain so injury doesn't slow us down in our fight or escape. They also have natural anti-inflammatory properties. Aerobic sports seem to release these substances more reliably than other activities.

In an earlier chapter, I mentioned that exercise and sports are an excellent way to sidetrack the fight-or-flight response of the automatic brain. Although the danger our brain perceives is as individual as we are, the fight-or-flight response is universally quite similar and indiscriminate. Danger our automatic brain senses, even on a subconscious level, creates stress throughout our body. As I have said, the fight of the AB often shows itself as aggressive behavior and the flight as passive. When we feel a need to fight or flee, exercise is often the most appropriate place to turn, especially with the fight reflex.

The effect of adrenaline and cortisol on our body is extremely detrimental over time unless we can put it to use. The only way to put it to good use, so that it does not injure our vascular system, is to use our muscles. Adrenaline and cortisol tend to cloud our thinking as they work hard to make sure our muscles can move fast. But with this fast movement comes the release of endorphins, which temporarily stops brain drain allowing the mind to peek through. With that comes the ability to think without effort. Thoughts just appear and solutions arise spontaneously. Running is a great exercise for this.

Since running on the road can be traumatic for our bones and joints, I suggest choosing surfaces that are more forgiving. If you choose to run on the road I suggest only one to three times a week for no more than three or four miles. This is a time when the power of your mind allows you to notice things you wouldn't normally notice—the breeze on your face, the swaying of the trees in the wind, the movement of birds and squirrels, or the occasional deer or turkey. Brisk walking, but not strolling, can accomplish the same. Additionally, bicycling is an excellent outdoor aerobic exercise with less joint trauma. Indoor, one can achieve aerobic fitness through an elliptical trainer or treadmill.

Running on the road can reveal your AB at work or that of another. Once while running, I noticed someone walking more slowly in front of me. I resisted "turning it up" and blowing passed her (rejecting the urgings of my AB) and kept my "mindful" steady pace. Naturally I did catch up with her and as I passed, in my steady moderate stride, she quipped, "Show-off!" Obviously, she felt one-upped, and this triggered her AB. (This is a great example of, no matter how hard you try not to be controlled by your AB, you still cannot control or be responsible for another's automatic brain).

For the fittest body, and thus mind, and thus ability to calm the AB, I advocate exercise diversity: aerobic activity, strength training, plus flexibility. Strength training need not cost any money and can be done at your desk or home using your own body weight. For example, dips in your chair at work, pushups in your family room while watching some TV show, or pull-ups using a bar placed in the door jamb of your bedroom closet. Both yoga and Pilates can augment this and will help with flexibility. Yoga especially can help you connect with your mind as it represents a form of moving meditation.

Sleep

In Chapter 15, I referred to that moment of awakening when we're not yet aware of what we need to be concerned about. This magical moment is free from the automatic brain. But if you had restless or too little sleep and you wake up on the wrong side of the bed, your magical moment will be ever so brief, the automatic brain robust and in charge. Finding the power of your mind in such a state becomes an uphill climb.

Getting the proper quantity and quality of sleep depends on many factors. In ancient times, humans had to worry about being vulnerable to attack by a predator animal or by another human. Those dangers are largely gone, but the automatic brain is still on guard. Just as with meditation, the automatic brain seeks to protect us from the vulnerability we might face during sleep. As I have discussed extensively throughout this book, the automatic brain developed to protect us from anything that represents danger or places us in a vulnerable position. When stimulated, the automatic brain causes us to fight or flee.

In the time of our prehistoric ancestors, sleep was not as safe as it is today. The automatic brain must have been on high alert, and the benefit of sleep was not much greater than the risk. Now, here we are in the 21st Century, and sleep to our automatic brain still represents the same potentially threatening situation it did thousands of years ago, one that we may need to fight or flee. This ancient mechanism helps explain why 60 million Americans suffer from sleep disorders! Sleep is a perfect time for the automatic brain to begin plotting strategies to deal with tomorrow's to-do list or think about the woulda, coulda, shouldas of yesterday. Sleep becomes "dangerous" as it takes away from these "vital" activities. I also propose that even when we do fall asleep, the activity of the automatic brain is responsible for dreaming. What the AB conjures up while we sleep is often related to some danger, threat, or vulnerability that we face during our wakeful hours. And therefore, for the most part, we should not believe, trust, or take direction from our dreams.

As I have said, in order to experience the power of our mind, we must not believe, trust, or take direction from the automatic brain as it tries to protect us. In Chapter 11, I pointed out the manipulation, seduction, and lies of our AB's protective mechanism. Nowhere is this more apparent then when we lie down and go to sleep. What we must realize is that anything (other than certain illnesses) that interferes with this normal human function is the product of the automatic brain trying to make you fight or flee sleep—to protect you.

In fact, I will take this a step farther. When lying down to sleep, if uneasiness or anxiety creeps in, consider it a sign that the automatic brain is trying to protect you from some danger—whether that danger is sleep itself, some other problem you may be facing, or a situation that has you stepping outside of your comfort zone. It's important to resist engaging the automatic brain, for doing so creates a vicious circle—you think about sleep all the time, which leads to daytime anxiety about what will happen next time you try to sleep. When the automatic brain is active, you might fall asleep only to be jolted awake almost immediately. Many patients have told me this happens to them, and I have experienced it myself. The antennae of the automatic brain detect a sudden vulnerability, and the AB suddenly awakes you as it goes into action. When the AB causes you sleep difficulties embrace it as a signal that you are actually heading in the right direction, the direction opposite of which the AB is pushing you. For example, if you are starting a new job and have difficulty sleeping, it is because the new job represents an unknown, something dangerous as defined by your automatic brain. Understand that your sleep difficulty is only because you are challenging yourself—a good thing, as you move in the right direction.

Sleep apnea is a disorder that causes interruptions in breathing during sleep. Studies estimate 15 million Americans suffer from this. My theory is that the automatic brain is responsible for the vast majority of cases, including those who actually have obstructed airways, possibly due to obesity. My feeling is the automatic brain is fighting strongly to keep a person from deep sleep, the most vulnerable of conditions. This push/pull phe-nomenon between the need to sleep and the AB's need to protect creates lapses in breathing; in a sense, a tug of war in which there is no winner.

If sleep is difficult for you I recommend you practice a meditation and/or breathing exercise as I described in Chapter 15. As you lie down to go to sleep, continue to focus on your breathing, and repeat a mantra with every breath. For example, "There is no danger, there is no threat." Do not believe, trust, or take direction from any impulse that tries to get you to do anything but go to sleep.

The way to connect your body with your spirit—your soul—is through the portal of the mind. A healthy body makes for a healthy mind, thus making this connection seamless and natural. Removing the obstruc-tion of the automatic brain by believing more in the opposite of what it directs, thus stopping brain drain makes for optimal health of your body, of your mind.

·

CHAPTER SEVENTEEN

Cultivate Your Mind

⚜

"Growth itself contains the germ of happiness."

–Pearl S. Buck

The challenge when living a life believing in the power of the mind rather than one controlled by the insistences of the automatic brain is to resist slipping back into the mire and muck of the AB. Sharpening your awareness of your mind through meditation and recognizing daily magic (see chapter 19) makes the task a little easier, but the challenge can appear daunting and even impossible. It just seems easier to live an AB-based life, because all you need as proof of its reality is provided by your senses and the physical reality that you experience daily.

In my view, a life of believing in your mind begins with the ability to maintain optimism and manage stress. Stress, of course, is a physical manifestation of the automatic brain, whereas optimism is the face of your belief in the power of your mind. The automatic brain is so pervasive that it takes constant effort to permit optimism to prevail. Fortunately, the activity of the AB is either black or white, on or off, so you can easily recognize its binary nature. If a threat to survival exists, the brain switches the AB on. But no threat = no activation.

You can reshape your mind so it does not perceive danger everywhere. Daily magic helps do this, and so does meditation. Humans have long sought ways to curb the automatic brain. Perhaps the most universal is music.

Pythagoras, of Pythagorean Theorem fame, was recognized during his time more as a philosopher than as a mathematician. He and his followers believed that numbers could form the basis of a universal philosophy. They identified three types of music: the music of instruments, the music of the human body and soul, and the music of the spheres (essentially the music of the cosmos). Linked to this philosophy were geometric shapes and orbiting motions; indeed, you could make a case that Pythagoras was the first proponent of "string theory" as a tool for understanding the universe. Through mathematics, the ultimate tool of the automatic brain, they proposed a mindful view of music—essentially bringing the mind (through music) into a form (mathematics) that we can understand. Suffice to say, Pythagoras believed that by bringing order to our physical world through mathematics and an understanding of logic and reason, we could achieve a more spiritual (or mindful) existence. Music was a major part of his and his followers' philosophy.

Even someone who is hearing impaired can appreciate music. After all, the creation of music—and how we feel or hear it—is simply the propagation of vibrations and waves. Beginning from the time in our mother's womb where we first heard the rhythm of the heartbeat, music has been part of our life experience. What I find fascinating is how these vibrations and waves of sound can affect the way we feel and our ability to understand the power of our mind.

Emotions are difficult to define scientifically. What we do know is that thoughts create our emotions, which create a flow of chemical electricity. As we look more closely into this flow, we find that it is nothing more than atom-sized particles making their way along nerve cells that are, just like everything else, made of atoms. Somehow, music affects this flow in a way that causes us to feel happy or sad.

Music's ability to make us feel is not related to our five senses. Thus it transcends the boundaries of our physical existence, which we cling to as proof of reality. In other words, it enters the realm of our mind—a realm that is not easily explained by the physical laws of our senses and automatic brain. Music can make us feel confident or anxious, powerful or fragile, optimistic or melancholy. Trying to predict what type of music should cause what type of feeling just makes it less authentic and reduces it from sublime mind to ordinary automatic brain.

There have been times while I was driving that I've felt I should also be doing something productive, like listening to a book on tape, listening to talk radio, listening to the news, talking with someone on the hands-free cell phone, or solving problems. We all juggle a million things at once, and we don't want to waste time. Each moment, after all, is precious, a gift—the present. We don't think of listening to music as accomplishing anything (blame the manipulation of the AB). Anytime our mood becomes sullen and our optimism wanes, we gravitate away from music and focus on thinking about our problems, or the news, say. But when we let music just nurture our mind, it actually balances us, making us less needy, and creates ideas, possibility, and confidence.

Some people refer to music as the universal language. Lyrics affect how we react to music, but the sounds and vibrations created by the artist transcend language. The tone alone can inspire exhilaration or sadness. The automatic brain can use the sound of music as a tool of domination, either by the artist or by the listener (the composer Richard Wagner and Hitler, for example). In other words, a musician can exert dominance over others, and people listening to music may be driven to act with AB-based behavior (for example, with violence). Or the listener can extract meaning from a particular artist to manipulate his or her agendas (again one thinks of the example of Richard Wagner and Hitler, or in a less dramatic and more subtle example, marketers using pop music. These two examples are mutually exclusive and I do not make any attempt to compare them, only to use them as two separate and distinct examples of how the automatic brain can manipulate such a pure cultivator of the mind).

To cultivate the power of your mind through music, you've got to practice feeling music. You'll recall that I became a drummer as an adult. First it was hand percussion, then acoustic (regular) drums. Most music has a certain rhythm, a certain regularity, a certain logic. Logical mathematical equations can explain the order of music (this began with Pythagoras). But what cannot be explained by mathematics is how music makes us feel.

Music represents a pristine example of how the mind can intersect with the "logic" of the automatic brain. It proves, in some ways, that the mind can operate on a level playing field with the AB in the realm of the physical; that it is not completely metaphysical. When I play drums, I attempt to play with my mind and not allow my automatic brain to obstruct the flow of my rhythm. If I believe the attempts of my AB to sabotage my efforts (believing that I am really vulnerable, hence a target for attack), then a thought comes up to question exactly what I am doing, which in turn leads to a brief mess-up, until of course I redirect my "feel."

To play music you have to train the mind. That training does not detract from the idea of the powerful mind. It further shows how the mind works very well within a framework of our normal, everyday lives. Musicians will tell you that the less they try, the less they think about what they are doing, and the more they feel what they are playing, the better is their experience and the more profound is the listener's experience. Of course, it takes a lot of dedication and practice to reach that point. When you look to music to cultivate your mind, but not as a musician, the moment defines the music. Whether that music is classical, heavy metal, classic rock, hip-hop, jazz, country, or rhythm and blues, the feeling defines your experience; the music does not define you.

There is no time in life where the automatic brain is stronger than during our teen years. During my own teens, I recall feeling uncomfortable revealing my taste in music. After all, you weren't supposed to like both rock and disco, or rock and the new genre known as rap. However, I submit that no music is actually repulsive if you feel it in the moment. If you despise rap or heavy metal, I suggest you turn down the volume and don't listen to the lyrics (as many lyrics are written from the influence of the automatic brain). Feel the rhythm and listen to the synchrony of the instruments. Try to feel the energy of the musicians. Paul Simon and Art Garfunkel recalled, while riding in a car in 1965, hearing the song "Sounds of Silence." They turned to each other and said, "Those guys sound like they're having fun!" For a moment, they did not recognize they were hearing their own first hit song.

Not everyone's taste in music is as eclectic as mine. To use music to connect with the power of your mind, I suggest starting with what you know you like. Avoid music that makes you reminiscent. Turn to music that inspires you. Even if music makes you sad, its emotional intensity can be inspiring if it proclaims the existence of something greater than our physical selves. Just to be clear, if the sadness you feel while listening to certain music is because of your memories, then I still suggest avoiding that music. The sadness about which I speak is more akin to tears of happiness and empowerment, than generating thoughts of regret or melancholy about the passage of time.

The music of Paul Potts elicits feelings, which may seem sad, but reaffirm the existence of something greater than our automatic brain. Paul Potts auditioned for the British television show *Britain's Got Talent* in 2007. Mr. Potts was an awkward, insecure 37-year-old man. As a child he had been victimized by bullies because of his slightly odd appearance. As he stood in front of the judges, they thought they were about to witness a man making a buffoon of himself—great for ratings (they know how to cash in on the automatic brain). Here was a 37 year-old, awkward man, timidly standing in front of them and telling them his dream was to sing opera.

As the judges rolled their eyes, Paul Potts, a mobile-phone salesman from Wales with no formal training, began singing *Nessun Dorma* in Italian. Even if you never felt opera was your thing (because I surely felt that way), Google "Paul Potts audition." I guarantee you will understand what I mean when I say music is a vehicle to understanding the greatness and power that exists beyond the automatic brain. I don't want to give too much away by saying more. Suffice it to say, the emotions you will experience while listening to his performance exist within the realm of your mind.

Music represents something very magical. For those who need continual reinforcement of the magic of our mind, just tune into music that inspires you—music that makes you feel like dancing, singing, saving the world, falling in love, music that makes you dream. It is no coincidence that as we feel more smothered by the realities of our automatic brain, we slip away from music. To reconnect with the power of your mind, turn to music.

Humor

Another factor in good health is the ability to laugh. There are many theories how it works, but one thing I know is that laughing makes me feel good. It is pretty hard to feel sad while laughing. That is why the automatic brain moves us away from humor when troubling circumstances face us. The AB views humor and laughter as a waste of time better spent planning how to deal with a situation. The automatic brain interprets laughing and being happy with having our guard down, thus vulnerable for attack.

As described in the December 4, 2003, issue of the medical journal Neuron, MRI imaging shows that humor stimulates specific areas of the brain, including the amygdale (which you'll recall is the primary storage place of danger memories). The stimulation does not reactivate danger memories that would lead to a fight-or-flight reaction. On the contrary, as we know from personal experience, it works to calm this reaction.

Other studies have shown that laughter reduces pain by producing pain killing hormones called endorphins. Additionally research has shown that laughter strengthens immune function by increasing the production of T-cells, interferon, and immune proteins called globulins. Laughter also can help tame the fight-or-flight response of the AB by helping to lower cortisol levels and returning our body to a more relaxed state.

Whether one believes in the Old Testament or not, the fact that it mentions humor indicates how long humankind has been aware of its power (Proverbs 17:22: "A merry heart doeth good like a medicine."). Or for those less inclined to turn to scripture, Groucho Marx offers his take on it: "A clown is like aspirin, only he works twice as fast."

When you feel happy, you essentially plug the brain drain and unleash the power of your mind. Place yourself in a position, the vulnerable position of laughing at yourself. This challenges the automatic brain and proves that by doing so, your mood improves and your mind becomes clearer. Thus, the opposite of what your AB feels you need.

Try staring in the mirror, put on a goofy smile, and make yourself laugh. I mean, put on the silliest smile you can muster, cross your eyes, try to look totally goofy. (This is why you should try this alone!). I'd be surprised if your mood doesn't improve.

Laughter Yoga schools are one of the fastest-growing forms of yoga (really!). A snapshot of me riding a roller coaster while vacationing caused me to laugh uncontrollably at myself. I sent this photo out to the thousands on my distribution list so they could laugh at and with me. Though the automatic brain looks down upon such self-deprecation, the mind feeds on it. We're attracted to public figures that appear vulnerable, humorous, and at times self-deprecating. The AB deems these attributes dangerous, but such behavior fosters our mind.

I recall, while a medical student on my surgical rotation, I worked with a particular funny and oftentimes silly surgical resident. Once, while wheeling a patient to the operating room, he asked the patient whether he was nervous about the operation. The patient, responded, "No, not really." The resident then retorted, "Phew, that's a good thing, because I sure am!" This resident was very skilled and confident and the patient knew he was joking. Such self-deprecation, though, can actually instill a sense of confidence in others. The automatic brain, if trusted, will have you think otherwise.

If you feel you have lost your sense of humor, rediscover it by watching reruns of the shows that used to make you laugh. In your daily activities, try to see something funny in situations that seem very serious. Your AB will have you believe that this is callous, but such levity can inspire calm and inner strength, focus, and surprising guidance. Yes, there are times when we need to mourn. These times should be limited, though, and to limit your mourning pays tribute to the person whose loss you mourn. Allow yourself to celebrate their life and your life, and laugh again.

Hobbies

In Chapter 8, I talked about how we define ourselves and how that nourishes our AB, ultimately keeping us from realizing our true desires. Cultivating essence means breaking out of stereotypes we hold about ourselves. Many of us avoid pursuing certain hobbies that are associated with the privileged, for example. If you harbor a danger memory about wealth and associate a certain sport—golf or tennis, say—with the wealthy, you may deprive yourself of learning to play those sports. That would be playing to your automatic brain, of course.

Danger memories help to establish our comfort zones as adults. For me, musicians once represented people with a lot of confidence and the ability to put themselves out there; qualities that were beyond the boundaries set by my own danger memories. These limitations are how we define ourselves; they prevent us from pursuing activities outside our self-imposed boundaries (in the Revelation Grid, boxes 2 and 3). Becoming a drummer, therefore, helped me push beyond the limitations of the automatic brain and helped guide me to believe in the power of my mind. Certainly, as I discussed earlier, I had to deal with my powerful AB trying to keep me narrowly defined and "safe".

The AB does not welcome time you spend away from the essential chores of your life. The automatic brain views leisure activities as threats to your ability to survive. Shunning leisure activity is part of the profile of the Type A personality—people so driven by work and obsessed with responsibilities that they are unable to take time out for a hobby. (On the other hand, there are those who do nothing but pursue leisure activities. They view work and personal responsibility as a threat, in a sense as their "hobby"; therefore, they flee work just as the Type A flees from the danger of leisure).

To maintain a healthy mind, you must realize where your personal danger memories lie and work not to believe, trust, or take direction from the related thoughts nor to plan how to fight or flee that danger. The more you can separate from your self-assigned definition, the more the flow of body, mind, and spirit can flow unabated. This for me defines growth. Though troubled or pressured from personal or professional obligations, the need to escape stagnation and grow can be an affirmation of living.

Re-exploring a previous passion or developing a new one puts you in a better position to deal with the challenges that the AB has you believing need your undivided attention. When the thought comes to mind, "I can't afford to do this," just replace it with "I can't afford not to do this." Whether "afford" refers to money or time, it represents a common manipulator of the AB.

Mondays

What do Mondays have to do with brain drain? Whether one is a student, an employee working outside the home, or a parent working inside the home, Monday signals the resumption of activity and heightened responsibility, much of which is unknown. A 10-year study published in the British Medical Journal found that 20 percent more people die of heart attacks on Monday than on any other day. Monday is perhaps the day of the week where brain drain is most apparent.

Sunday evening, too, can be a time of increased anxiety. I am not talking about full-blown panic, but rather an undercurrent of uneasiness that causes restlessness and can interfere with sleep. What is it about Sunday evening? It is the prelude to the beginning of a new cycle. Just ahead lies the unknown. What will the new workweek bring? Since the automatic brain looks out to protect our body from danger, the unknown has the potential to trigger the response to fight or flee. That's what's behind the uneasiness, anxiety, and stress (the face of the AB) of Sunday evening.

One of my patients, a teacher, told me the same phenomenon applies to summer vacation, something that meshes with my own recollections as a student. She explained, "June is like Friday night, July is Saturday night, and August is Sunday night."

Poor Monday—blue Monday, to some—seems to be the least popular day of the week. Wednesday is of course the hump day, and TGIF means the weekend is here. The point is that what kind of mood we are in often depends on what day it is. Monday morning comes around and our mood may be melancholic. We start rolling the boulder up the emotional hill until Friday night, when it rolls down without much resistance. That's the time that we start building up resistance again and the cycle starts anew as it reaches its lowest point on Monday morning. That is also the time that our bodies and minds start feeling the resistance.

The face of our mind is optimism—an inner confidence that no matter what, everything will work out as it should. To allow this feeling to flow unrestrained, we need to keep our emotions balanced. Being aware that the calendar and clock form a vital platform from which the automatic brain exerts its force lets you glimpse how you might accomplish this.

Maybe you could make Monday a date night with your significant other, when you watch a comedy, listen to music, or be intimate. Many restrict sexual intimacy to the weekend, but why not dedicate another night during the week? I suggest Monday! That will really give you something to look forward do, boost your mood, and, believe it or not, will allow your mind to flow more easily.

The feelings you get by cultivating your mind cannot be easily explained by the logic and practicality on which the automatic brain relies. The more you experience these sensations that exist beyond the limits of the AB, the more you see that they fit comfortably within the 'real" world. This will allow you to further cultivate your mind and more reliably depend on it as your guide.

CHAPTER EIGHTEEN

Death, Dying, Quantum Physics, and Possibility

✦✦✦

*"Not only is the universe stranger than we imagine,
it is stranger than we can imagine"*

–Arthur Stanley Eddington

Throughout our lives, people close to us die. One day they're here, the next moment they're gone. This experience is as human as eating and breathing. As a physician for more than 20 years, I am inevitably around death and dying. I have developed the ability to be fully in the moment with the family of someone who is dying or recently deceased and, in the next moment, to transition to the routine of everyday life. I do not consider this a callous act, but instead a celebration of the dying person's life, of that person's living family, and of the universality of life and death.

Just because I can separate myself from the grief and move back into life does not mean I am insensitive to death. On the contrary, I am fascinated by the concept of death, and neither in a morbid nor coldly clinical way. Surrounded by death throughout my career, I have had no choice but to think about it a lot, and to ponder where we come from (beyond the birds and bees stuff, of course!), why we are here, and where we go when we die.

Obsessing over death is an extreme behavior, and the work of the automatic brain. Preventing our death is the primary purpose of the AB, so death is its failure. The mere thought that death might involve something beyond our physical body is anathema to the automatic brain. Death represents the epitome of nothingness and represents the ultimate uncharted territory; the very thought of death triggers a powerful fight-or-flight response.

When the NBC political analyst Tim Russert died, a frequently heard comment was, "He died before his time." What that really meant, coming as it did from the protective automatic brain, was that he died before *our* time. There is no good time for death, according to the automatic brain. It is all bad, because it symbolizes failure. In the reality of our mind, Tim Russert died at precisely his time, the same as everyone does.

Our greatest limiting factor, the single greatest obstruction to the free flow of energy between body, mind, and spirit, in my opinion, is the work of the automatic brain, which forever prevents us from contemplating anything beyond direct sensory experience. After all, that is how we interact and know our world, which is how we protect ourselves, that is how we maintain life. According to the automatic, reflexive brain, experience from the senses is all we need for the survival of our physical being. What we see is what we get. The irony is that the automatic brain relies on anything but what is tangible—thoughts (not something we can touch and feel), the non-physical past, or future possibilities.

You might think that the here and now would be the domain of the AB, since the here and now is concrete, what we experience with our senses, what is real. But the here and now rarely poses a direct threat. The danger is in thoughts about the past and the future – what your mind conjures up, and these are really little more than a fantasy. Thoughts how your life would turn out if your past were different is sheer conjecture and the future is mere speculation—a creation of our mind, our automatic brain, hence fantasy. These are the domain of the AB from which it derives its power and its ability to limit our mind—when we believe, trust, and take direction from it. And it's why I feel so passionate about the need to understand the automatic brain. The power of our mind represents the conduit between our living spirit that's not limited by the laws of logic and reason, which our automatic brain has created in order to protect, preserve, and replicate our physical body. Thinking about spiritual concepts, including death and the afterlife, is a threat too great for our AB to bear.

From our early years, we know that the death of our physical body is inevitable. Our automatic brain has evolved the way it has precisely to stave off death as long as necessary to spread our DNA, so that we may assure the survival of our genetic identity. The concept of birth, death, and the inexorable march of time fits geometric principles that describe the world in three dimensions. The principle that is missing—the fourth dimension, if you will—is the question of, what really dies? We are composed of atomic and subatomic particles—cells, matter. This matter contains an enormous amount of energy that's not dependent on circulating blood or oxygen delivery. Energy cannot be destroyed, only transformed from one type to another (e.g., from light to heat). When we die, the matter that was our body still exists, though in a form that gradually becomes unrecognizable, but what about the energy?

Death is clearly the extinction of our physical body and the end of our ability to replicate our DNA. However, is it the death of our being? Since we are mostly energy, perhaps death is merely the end of a portion of that being, the minor portion. Consider the possibility that the greater part of our being, the one that makes itself known to us throughout our lives, through our mind, is not destroyed.

Pythagoras, Einstein, and Quantum Physics
Humankind has contemplated its existence through the evolution of the neocortex. Because of the power of the automatic brain, which we acquired a few hundred thousand years ago, our greatest modern challenge has been to calm it and remove its influence on out thought and

behavior. Some of history's greatest thinkers would invoke drastic measures to do so. For example, Pythagoras formed a sort of religious cult on the Greek island of Samos around 530 BC. The Pythagoreans were a contemplative society, and often were not allowed to speak, as that would interfere with their contemplation.

Pythagoras was one of the first to suggest that the thought processes and the soul were located in the brain and not the heart. He believed that the essence of being is found in numbers, and that being relies on the mathematical stability of the universe. Things like health rely, he said, on a stable proportion of elements; too much or too little of one thing causes an imbalance that makes a being unhealthy.

Numbers were the central theme in Pythagoras's thinking and that of his followers. The philosophy evolved into a belief that knowledge of the essence of being can be found in the form of numbers. Taking this a step further, we can say that because mathematics is an unseen essence, the essence of being is an unseen characteristic that can be revealed by the study of mathematics.

So which came first, mathematics or the physical universe that mathematics explains? Interestingly, the automatic brain is able to engage and use mathematics, through probability and statistics, to establish what we should trust in and believe. In Pythagoras's world, mathematics was used to open the door to an understanding of that which we do not readily sense. Mathematics puts the metaphysical into a language we can understand. It does not conflict with the metaphysical or the concept of mindfulness or the power of our mind, it simply exposes it in a temporal language. In the view of Pythagoras and his followers, once essence, through numbers, was assimilated into our physical lives, we could transcend the physical, rational, logical world in favor of a spiritual place not governed by conventional laws. He believed this would allow reincarnation and what he called the transmigration of souls—the ability of our

soul to become one with another living person or animal or even inani-
mate object. That wasn't all: his followers theorized that souls would cease
reincarnation once they had lived a moral life. After that, they would exist
eternally in the spiritual world.

Was Pythagoras on to something? Is that why we are here—to transform our automatic brain driven, reactive existence into one based on the
ability of our mind to serve as a portal to spirituality, the link between
body and spirit? Is this a way in which our inner guidance, our divine
spirit, our mind can assimilate with the physical world?

Fast-forward about 2,400 years, and Albert Einstein is born. As I
have said, Einstein's abilities were due much less to his rote intelligence
than to his ability to see beyond the senses. Einstein explains his theory
"… that mass and energy are both…manifestations of the same thing. A
somewhat unfamiliar conception for the average mind…Very small
amounts of mass may be converted into a very large amount of energy and
visa versa." In my view, his reference to the average mind refers more
accurately to the automatic brain. In any case, his ideas opened the door
to quantum physics and the notion that something (mass) can be created
out of nothing (energy). This titanic scientific mind also revealed that
mass (the physical) can create energy, and that atomic and subatomic particles can appear in two places at once. Even the manipulation, seduction,
and lies of our automatic brain have trouble refuting Einstein's theories,
because they were proven in the language of the automatic brain, through
mathematics and physics.

Einstein's theories and later proofs suggest a world far different from
anything our automatic brain can conceive. If mass (a quality of matter,
something that can be measured) can be converted into energy, and
thoughts are simply the movement of electrically charged atoms (with
mass), then theoretically the energy generated through the mass of moving atoms can create the energy of thought. To Einstein, that energy might

then be converted into mass—something tangible, something we can wrap our hands around and call real.

Our automatic brain is primitive and more suited to protect us when danger is finite and involves only physical threats. With the development of our advanced mind came the ability to add another layer of danger. The logical cause-and-effect nature of our AB is of little use in the Einsteinian universe, which is much different from what we can observe through our physical, sensory evidence. Bottom line, understanding that mass can create energy and energy can create mass is illogical to the automatic brain but logical and rational to our mind.

Einstein's four-dimensional space-time, which he used for his relativity-related mathematical computations, defies ordinary human comprehension. Relativity cannot be deduced from empirical or practical measurements, but is derived from mathematical computations. Pythagoras believed that mathematics was the language of essence, a language we could understand, one that even our automatic brain can understand. Conceivably, Einstein began to show this. As Einstein once declared, "The distinction between past, present, and future is merely an illusion—albeit a stubborn one."

Thoughts and Relative Time

I recall one day sitting in class during medical school, and looking at my watch because the lecture was so boring. It seemed to go on forever. Of course in reality, it was the same 50 minutes as every other class. The next day, the material in the lecture was fascinating, and the 50 minutes seemed to fly by. Not once did I look at my watch. The experience flowed smoothly, with what seemed like a lot happening in a very short period of time. This is how dreams work—a lot happening in only a few seconds or minutes of actual elapsed time. We plan our days, our weeks, our months, our years, our lives according to clock time. The clock ticks away and we move right along with it.

Most biologists agree that the cells in our bodies have a relatively fixed life span—roughly 70 to 100 years. Our brains are governed by circadian rhythms based on a 24-hour period and controlled in part by the comings and goings of light. Time marches on, caring not at all about our cells. Our electrons circle around the nuclei of our atoms and our DNA replicates, disconnected from the secondhand on our wristwatch.

Our thoughts are intangible creations of our mind and generate energy, so they must cause some type of reaction. Could it be that the energy generated by our thoughts creates a reaction in the cells of our body? Since we know that positive thoughts make us feel better, perhaps the reaction occurs at a cellular level, leading to a feeling of well-being, longevity, and even health. Let me take this idea one step further. If energy can create mass, and mass (the physical world) is what we experience with our senses, can it be that the energy of thought can make manifest or create things in our sensory experience? Maybe, it fits with the notion that visualizing your dreams and aspirations can convert them into reality. But, herein lies a big distinction. The mind, body, spirit connection is just that; it is not the automatic brain, body, spirit connection (as I pointed out earlier). The latter blocks the free flow of energy between body and spirit, while the mind channels that energy. The automatic brain does not generate original thought. It simply rearranges stored memories, from which it projects the future. Therefore, the negativity of the automatic brain does not result in your attracting negative into your life. It serves as roadblock to the free flow of positive thoughts and ideas originating in your mind. The power of your mind is what, I believe, can alter cellular energy and result in you attracting those things that are right for you.

Simply adopting the view, as Einstein did, that time and matter does not limit our experience opens up a universe of possibilities. They're antithetical to the automatic brain, because there are no clear boundaries; too many grey areas. The AB is a binary operator, sort of like a computer. Information is entered (circumstance referenced against danger memories), and that turns on or off the AB. It strictly follows the laws of cause and effect, and views the world in Euclidean terms (three-dimensional). The mind, though, is unlimited, infinite, and taps into a powerful reality defined by an energy stream that the automatic brain cannot comprehend. Einstein's universe is based on non-Euclidean geometric models and reveals the possibility of other dimensions.

What fascinates me is that the automatic brain is quick to dismiss the "magic" of the mind, but it is also quick to employ components of the mind as a means to its end (survival of the individual body). For example, the creation of the atom bomb comes directly out of Einstein's theory that great energy exists even in the smallest of mass (atomic and sub-atomic particles). The expression of the automatic brain is the fight-or-flight response, represented by human aggression or passivity. The automatic brains of so many seek to turn atomic energy into aggression. And automatic brain decisions always end up unsatisfactorily in the end.

You may feel that disagreements and war are always driven by the automatic brain. But to preserve and nourish our mind, we must demonstrate the behavior of our mind, which is assertiveness. When faced with aggression from someone out to destroy you, you must remain assertive—not angry, aggressive, or passive; just strong, powerful, with calm energy. Self-defense is an example of assertiveness.

The martial arts, in their pure form, are good examples of this distinction. They call upon the mind through the energy of Qi (pronounced chee, or key), or "life force."

Our mind speaks to us in our daily lives in a language that should be recognized by the automatic brain. But the incessant activity of the automatic brain does not allow us to notice it. Over the past 200,000 years or so, there was little challenge to the automatic brain and in fact, it was all we required. Our experience of the world was simply cause and effect, with the sole priorities of protecting our physical body and assuring survival of our DNA. Einstein's theories did not change the universe 100 years ago. They just raised the possibility that all along, the narrow view through the eyes of our AB may have mistakenly confined us to a reality that ends with the destruction of physical matter.

The real world, in fact, is beyond three dimensions, beyond the limits of our senses, beyond physical experience, and beyond the comprehension of our automatic brain. It is a world that speaks to us daily in some forms that we can recognize and some we cannot, through daily magic and the law of attraction. In this world, spiritual energy is limitless and eternal. The mind is our gateway to it. In life, this realization gives us the power to break through the limits imposed by our automatic brain, so we can create a tangible reality that we can believe, trust, and take direction from. In death, the idea of eternal existence, in some form, is a genuine possibility. It may not be a possibility that our "average" brains can easily comprehend, yet it remains quite compelling, to an open mind. To deny this possibility is to presume that what we know now, in the early 21st century, is all there is to know. Isn't that a silly presumption? After all, we still do not even know what gravity is. We know what it does, but we do not know what it is, really. A few hundred years ago, the best and the brightest thought the world was flat. Let us not continue to let our average brains block the flow of true greatness. Allow yourself to release the power of your mind.

CHAPTER NINETEEN

Daily Magic

❧❦❧

"Coincidences are God's way of remaining anonymous."

–Albert Einstein

About 3,200 years ago, according to traditional historical accounts, the Pharaoh Ramses II released the Israelites from their 400-year enslavement. This release was not voluntary. During that time, according to religious belief, God through Moses inflicted 10 plagues upon Egypt, greatly motivating Pharaoh to release the Jews. You could make the case that anyone who experienced such events would quickly become a believer. Still, after 400 years of slavery, it took at least 10 plagues to persuade even the Jews that something supernatural was happening.

Once released from Egyptian bondage, the Jews, lead by Moses, began their trek to the Red Sea. Hot on their heels were Pharaoh and his troops, who had second thoughts about losing all those slaves. According to the legend, Moses split the sea with his staff, allowing the Jews to pass safely and then collapsing the walls of water upon the pursuing Egyptians. Arriving at Mt. Sinai, Moses went up the mountain and received the Ten Commandments. He was gone for several weeks and the Jewish people became doubtful, constructing a golden calf to worship, essentially giving up on Moses and his God. Many of you know how the story ends, and I'll wrap up my biblical narrative at this point.

Imagine if, through your five senses, you had witnessed 10 awesome and unexplainable events. Imagine that even if you doubted the divine origin of those events, to top it off you came to what looked like certain sudden death, yet as if by magic you were able to pass safely while your pursuers perished. Would you then, for the rest of your life, believe in miracles? And would you believe that you are somehow connected with the universe so that your mind and spirit are intertwined and you possess the ability to exert tremendous force on the material world around you?

Have you, figured out why the Israelites doubted Moses even after witnessing those impressive miracles? Remember a little thing called the automatic brain? (I've only mentioned it a zillion times!) Through manipulation, seduction, and lies the automatic brain attempts to shield us all from the danger of anything it decides is impractical or implausible according to physical laws. Our ancestors, who knew little of the physical laws of science, nevertheless knew what they saw, heard, touched, smelled, and tasted, and that sensory input is all the AB needs to establish reality and sense danger. Miracles are incompatible with the automatic brain; they threaten its authority, thus representing a threat to our physical survival.

How does the power of our mind show up in our everyday existence? How do we bring it into our reality, into a form we understand?

What most of us think of as a miracle is some kind of supernatural occurrence: 10 plagues being visited upon our enemy, the parting of the Red Sea, winning the lottery, or some other apparently divine intervention that exists outside our sensory experience of reality. We live our lives with preconceived notions of what constitutes a miracle, and figure we'll surely know one when we see one. But I suspect that even if we did experience a miracle that fit our criteria, unless the miracle happened repeatedly, we would begin to doubt it. Most of us do not really believe we have witnessed miracles, yet our thirst to see one remains boundless.

Miracles are the stuff that bridges the mind and spirit. This surreal concept threatens the automatic brain. So when occasional improbabilities occur, we chalk it up to coincidence.

During my career as a doctor, I have encountered many patients who defy the odds, avoiding death or disability despite the best predictions of modern medicine. Madeline was a 72-year-old woman and smoker for more than 50 years. Soon after she became my patient, we diagnosed her with lung cancer that was large and had already spread to her liver and brain. From all appearances, Madeline had little time to live.

Except for some breathlessness, though, she remained at the time of diagnosis remarkably sharp, comfortable, and strong. I said to her, "Whatever you decide to do, whether it is to receive chemotherapy or not, you need to believe 100 percent that you have made the right decision. Never doubt your decision even if you start to feel ill." She decided to receive aggressive chemotherapy. I did not discourage her.

As Madeline began several rounds of chemotherapy, I worked with her to visualize the effects of the powerful medications. As a homemaker, she was able to envision the chemotherapy as a blast that was cleaning her house, and saw herself vacuuming up the debris of killed cancer cells. Within three months, the tumor in her lung had become undetectable, and there were no signs of the liver and brain metastases. Unfortunately, logic and conventional medicine guided her cancer doctors and they persuaded her to undergo one last round of chemotherapy to complete the regimen. That turned out to be her last dose; she died two weeks later from complications entirely related to the chemotherapy.

Undeniably, chemotherapy had played a role in Madeline's improvement. But nothing in modern medicine explains the extent of the response she had, especially the disappearance of her brain metastasis, upon which chemotherapy should have had no effect. Would she have survived if she had not received the last round of chemotherapy? I do not know; perhaps. But what I learned from my brief relationship with Madeline is that the power of our mind, and its connection to a greater power, trumps all; because it is not ruled by time nor nullified by physical death. The other doctors involved in Madeline's care may have looked upon her death as proof that silly mind games are no match for reality, but I know otherwise. To me, I witnessed a miracle while caring for her, and I'll never forget it.

As you know by now, the dominant automatic brain surveys the landscape for signs of impending danger. So most of the time, automatically and below our level of awareness, we are on guard. That interferes with the natural flow of energy between body, mind, and spirit, not to mention causing us to miss the enormity of events swirling around us. Though below our level of awareness, some may consider many of them, well, miraculous. Sometimes a simple change of perspective or focus can open the door to reveal miracles in a form we understand.

What would happen if you decided you want a bright green car because you do not recall seeing many of this color on the road, and you want to be unique, to make a statement. I suspect that once you started driving that car, you would see many green cars, similar to the one you just bought. Why? Because all of a sudden hundreds of people ran out and bought green cars when they found out you bought one? I don't think so. Rather, now you have brought the concept of *bright green cars* to a level of awareness, and you see more clearly what has been in front of you all along.

A seemingly meaningless event happened to me one summer afternoon while lying on a couch in the basement of my childhood house in New Haven. I was home from college; it was a Saturday afternoon. The day was hot and hazy and I fell asleep while watching a ballgame. I had plans to go out with some friends later that evening. As I went for my car keys, they were nowhere. I searched all over the house but could not find them. I continued to retrace my steps, and after a half hour or so, I got back to the couch. Removing the cushion, I saw the keys resting on the fabric.

That's it—nothing spiritual or cosmic, just a set of car keys that fell out of my pocket while I watched a ballgame. It was a moment, though, when I wondered what other events might be going on beyond my level of awareness.

The following story is paraphrased from various reports I have read:

On a cold January morning in 2007, at Washington, DC Metro Station, a man with a violin played six Bach pieces for about 45 minutes. During that time approx. 2 thousand people went through the station, most of them on their way to work. After 3 minutes a middle aged man noticed there was a musician playing. He slowed his pace and stopped for a few seconds and then hurried to meet his schedule. A few minutes later the violinist received his first dollar: a woman threw the money in the hat and, without stopping, continued to walk. Another few minutes passed and a young man leaned against the wall to listen to him, then looked at his watch and started to walk again. Ten minutes passed and a 3-year old boy stopped but his mother tugged him along hurriedly. The kid stopped to look at the violinist again, but the mother pushed hard and the child continued to walk, turning his head all the time. This action was repeated by several other children. Every parent, without exception, forced their children to move on quickly. The musician played continuously. Only 6 people stopped and listened for a short while. About 20 gave money but continued to walk at their normal pace. The man collected a total of $32.

After one hour of playing he finished and silence took over. No one noticed. No one applauded, nor was there any recognition.

No one seemed to know, but the violinist was Joshua Bell, one of the greatest musicians in the world. He played one of the most intricate pieces ever written, with a violin worth $3.5 million dollars. Two days before Joshua Bell sold out a theater in Boston where the seats averaged $100.

This is a true story. Joshua Bell played incognito in the metro station organized by the Washington Post as part of a social experiment. The questions raised: in a common place environment at an inappropriate hour, do we perceive beauty? Do we stop to appreciate it? Do we recognize talent in an unexpected context? How many other things are we missing?

Recently my sons got into an argument because one accused the other of taking his towel. Shortly afterwards, my older son found the towel he was looking for, right in front of him, draped over the back of a chair. He later came to me and acknowledged that he now understood what I meant when I talked about focus. He said that he had been so focused on arguing with his brother that he didn't see what was right in front of him.

To begin seeing miracles in our daily life, and hence reveal the power of our mind to attract what is right for us, it is important to retrain our focus. For the most part, self-preservation is our goal, so our focus is on thoughts created by the automatic brain. Any events we perceive as negative raise the odds of a vulnerable situation lurking. That fires up the automatic brain, further sharpening our focus so that we understand the negative event, inside and out, with perspective from past experience, and plotting future strategies.

Our protective brain wants always to prepare us for what is about to come—usually the worst-case scenario. Its intense focus on the current event blocks any chance we'll be aware of an unseen benefit, which the AB categorizes as improbable, impractical, and frankly dangerous. Believing, trusting, and taking direction from this restraining force actually makes us less prepared and less sensible (remember manipulation, seduction, and lies).

Just labeling an event as negative actually precludes the possibility of a positive outcome. The old adage—when one door closes another one opens—is another way of looking at this. However, when the automatic brain is our trusted security guard, that door remains locked with a sensitive alarm system and impenetrable deadbolt.

To begin opening the door and understanding the power of our mind, in a form with which you can feel and connect, I recommend keeping a journal. Let's call this journal "Daily Magic." Just as the Revelation Grid reveals how the AB manipulates us to believe we need it for protection, the Daily Magic journal helps reveal the power of our mind that already exists all around us, but what we may not readily see.

What goes in the journal is not a means to an end; it just is. Magical moments awaken your sensibilities to the swirling activity that surrounds all of us, which we usually fail to notice. Einstein predicted great energy exists in matter below our sensory awareness. Freud revealed that mental activity below our level of consciousness (awareness) controls much of human behavior. Keeping a journal helps you awaken your senses to reveal magic in an understandable form.

Journal entries may contain events that seem inconsequential. For example, a phone call from an old friend at the precise moment you were thinking of him. Or a special song on the radio that fits with something you were just thinking about. Maybe a hawk that glides across your field of vision as you look at the road ahead. Or an unexpected check that comes in the mail. Each day I awaken with an expectation that magic will happen. I do not look for it—I expect it. I do not predetermine what must happen to make my list, I expect that events will let me know whether they belong on my list. To understand how magical these events really are, just think what had to happen in your day for your life to intersect at precisely that moment when the "coincidence" occurs. Years ago while on vacation, we made a few wrong turns and then righted ourselves as we drove down the main street of the vacation town. Just as we entered the town we stopped at the crosswalk for a man to pass. As he walked across, I recognized that man as my roommate from college! The statistical, "logical" automatic brain would place enormous, if not impossible, odds against that happening. If our arrival was a few seconds either side of that moment, we would have missed him. What had to happen in my life and his life for our moment to intersect is in itself at the level of statistical improbability; rather magical, I must say.

When you make an entry, be aware that all events stand on their own, at the moment they occur. Neither past needs and wants nor future expectations should influence the entry. In other words, try not to think too much about your journal entries. Anything that feels like a coincidence, good or bad, you should enter. After you make an entry, resist going back and looking it over to see if it meant anything. In order to allow the energy of circumstance to flow unabated, resist listening to the "protective" mind of your AB.

It is important to write down events as they happen. Keep scrap paper in your pocket. Or set up a document on your computer at work. Assemble your notes at the end of your day and enter them into your journal, or enter them in your computer document as they happen (as I do on my laptop). Make sure you write them down! Simply making a mental note will not work well, as the automatic brain helps us easily forget. At first, you may have only a few items that make it to your list, but soon the list will grow large. In a six month period, my list is thirty-five pages long. As the list grows, you will be creating a reality that may not be comprehensible at first, but is fully recognized by your mind and inner guidance.

I recall a joke told to me once. During a terrible flood, a man perched himself on his rooftop for safety from the rising waters. A woman rowed by on her boat and said, "Hop in, I'll row you to a safe place." He replied, "No thanks, God will help me." She continued on. An hour later, another man rowed by, and shouted, "Hop in, I'll row you to a safe place." The man looked at the water now almost at his feet and retorted, "God will help me, thanks anyway." Another hour past and the water was up to his chin. The final boat passed and offered to take him aboard, but he rejected for the same reason. In heaven he met God and confused asked, "God, what's going on? I had so much faith in you and you didn't save me!" God responded, "Son, what more did you want? After all, I sent three boats!" Sometimes the magic is right in front of us, yet our automatic brain blocks our ability to recognize it.

You may wonder if a journal entry has relevance to your life. I suggest you avoid judging coincidences and looking for meaning behind them. Allow them to stand on their own. As you sharpen your focus and become more aware, you will seem to be attracting coincidences. Some may mean something, some may mean nothing. But the karma that you create will be one that reinforces the belief in your mind's power. Even during the most mundane days, you will find yourself expecting daily magic. As your daily magic journal grows, you will create the miracles that you desire, and they will be in a form that you easily recognize. You will then know that you have begun to connect with a deeper truth, one that will guide you, one in which you believe 100 percent.

PART III

Seven Days to Belief

Seven Days to Belief

✦❧✦

Although you will recognize many of the concepts in this section, I have organized them in a way so you can begin implementing them as soon as possible.

Throughout this book, I call upon readers to believe, trust, and take direction from their mind rather than the false protector—the automatic brain. This of course is easier said than done. After all, 200,000 years of evolution is hard to break through. Our genes are set firmly and deeply at birth, and our automatic brain grows to protect us from potential danger that could lead to our demise. The sole purpose of this system is to insure that we survive to pass along our DNA. There are two pretty big implied assumptions of this system: first, that even the smallest dangers can quickly snowball to the threat of death; and second, that passing on our DNA will lead to our immortality. Our brain has evolved to help us avoid (fight and flee) the worst-case scenario—our mortality, our death.

There are other things you should know about this system. The automatic brain is either on or it is off. If the antennae pick up danger, the system turns on; if no danger, it is off. When it turns on, it leads to a fight-or-flight response, which includes both physical and mental activity. The overt behavior it leads to is either aggressive (the fight), or passive (the flight). The reaction to perceived danger is reflexive and automatic. The reaction is strong and persuasive, telling us that this brain will do what-ever it takes to protect us. Employing manipulative thoughts, seductive scenarios, and outright lies, our automatic brain works 24/7 to keep us in a safe and secure place.

Although danger is different for everyone and is usually not as obvi-ous as a direct attack, the basic mechanics of the automatic brain are the same for everyone. The way our automatic brain processes potential dan-ger, and forms "danger memories" develops during childhood and endures into adulthood. In earlier chapters, I explained that most of our decision-making and behavior stems from our belief, trust, and direction-taking from this brain. As I also emphasized, the guidance it gives us is mostly misguided and not to be trusted.

Since this brain has such a pervasive influence on our lives, I am convinced that it stands in the way of our ability to see anything beyond it. It causes us to think of the unknown as always dangerous and threaten-ing. The future is the greatest of unknowns, and this brain incessantly directs us to attempt to predict it, in an effort to make it less unknown. Though its primary *raison d'être* is to protect us from that worst-case sce-nario, often this drift into the unknown future is a worst-case scenario. The result, ironically, is that we become more afraid now and less pre-pared. Such is the misguidance.

How do we stop this automatic brain from controlling our lives, from draining us of optimism and our zest for life? In other words, how do we stop brain drain? How do we deal with a brain that is falsely trying to protect us and keep us "safe" in our comfort zone? How do we believe in the power of our mind? How do we believe totally that, when our auto-matic brain fires up and tries to pull us back from danger, that danger from which it tries to protect us, is actually the precise direction of our true nature, our spiritual self, our essence? How do we believe that totally and without any doubt?

How can we believe that something that, on the surface, seems bad can actually be what is right for us? How can we believe that the greatest danger of all to our automatic brains—death—is not a danger to be feared? How can we believe that death is not the end? How do we really, really believe *that*?

I make the distinction between the automatic *brain* and our *mind*. Removing the automatic brain's blockade of dangers allows the free flow of energy between body, mind, and spirit. This creates the greatest attracting force in the universe and flows through us, and resides within all of us. It allows our mind to believe in phenomena outside the limits of our automatic brain, forming the foundation of belief and authentic faith.

How often do you start your day, your week with a sense of belief and faith, yet events happen or thoughts occur that diminish it? Many people say they believe in God or karma or the "law of attraction", but nothing seems to change in their lives, and they don't understand why.

To stop brain drain, once and for all, hinges on belief; hence, the reason for this last section, Seven Days to Belief. My hope is that this plan can lead you to an unshakeable belief—one that will transform your thinking, remove the obstacle of the automatic brain, and allow abundance to flow into your life.

Day One

Preparing your mind means allowing it to appear through the quagmire and confusion set forth by the swirling dangers incessantly triggering our automatic brain (AB). These dangers are not only danger memories forged in our past, but are reinforced by present dangers. When you become convinced that danger surrounds you, you become forever played by your AB. One of the most effective methods to begin the process of preparing your mind is to stop looking for danger. Your AB has one purpose - to protect you. When you truly need it, it will work just fine without you looking for it (remember Archie in chapter 12).

At the start of your day, upon awakening, **ask yourself the question,** *"What am I going to do today to believe in the power of my mind?"* Do not actively look for an answer.

As of today, **you will stop watching the news, including the business news, and be very selective in what news you choose to read.** In general, you should avoid most local headline stories. The news has become the modern version of elevator music—it's constantly in the background, to the point where we are numb to it. This opens us up to a contradiction and falsity: we believe to protect ourselves, we need more and more news information. The news becomes background noise that only makes us less aware and less alert. The more we rely on the AB, the less chance our mind will be awakened. The more we feed the AB, believe, trust, and take direction from it to "protect" us, the more stress we feel, the harder it becomes to be optimistic and believe.

News programs and stories often dwell on tragedy and drama as a way to draw in viewers, constantly upping the ante as our AB gets more desensitized. Local news programs are notorious for this, and at the risk of losing their support for my book, I suggest you tune them out! When you're in the car, avoid listening to all-news radio. During their broadcasts, human tragedy becomes a 30-second sound bite. A double homicide is mixed in with the sports and weather. Talk radio, generally, is more about the AB of the host than it is about real change.

Do not look at your bank statement, checking account balance, investment account, retirement account, whatever on this day. Plan only to look at these things when you are balancing them or after you have made a withdrawal or deposit. When you believe 100 percent that you have the ability to draw in all that is right for you, you will pick up the news, including business, which you need to know without having to look for it.

If you find yourself driving, play or **tune into music** that makes you want to sing and drum along on the steering wheel. Alternatively, **listen to a comedy** station on satellite radio or play a comedy CD. The same for television programming.

Throughout your day, **smile inside**. I mean feel and see yourself smiling from inside your chest. Picture your smiling face inside your chest around heart level.

Meditation is the best way to connect with your true inner guide. As the days go on, I will explain how to develop this. It is one of the key elements of developing belief. Today you will start your first **meditation** exercise. You will find 5 minutes in your day – just 5 minutes – and go to a quite place. You will close your eyes, and breathe deeply, in through the nose and out through the mouth. Preparing your mind means becoming aware of how your AB is blocking your awareness through false protective dangers. As you do this exercise expect many thoughts to race through your brain. This is the perfect exercise to begin seeing how the AB operates. When you relax into meditation, the AB goes into overdrive and conjures up many blocking thoughts to prevent the relaxation. Why would it act this way? Because the act of relaxation and meditation leaves you vulnerable to attack. The AB doesn't care that the likelihood of being attacked while meditating is negligible. The AB is binary – on or off, black or white. It simply reverts to the primitive survival patterns. We need to recognize, though, that the distracting thoughts that creep into our mind as we relax into meditation are among the same dangers that your AB references when you attempt to believe in yourself and your abilities. They represent the limits to your growth and are at the heart of your self-sabotage. They stand in the way of the natural flow of abundance. **Make note of the thoughts** but do not believe or react to them even if you think they have some merit. Recite in your mind, "**I believe 100 percent** in my ability to attract into my life everything that is right for me." Not 25 percent or 50 percent or 99 percent, but 100 percent. The only way you can begin to believe this is by rejecting the automatic, false protecting thoughts coming from your AB.

Before going to sleep, **declare**, *"There is no danger in my belief. I believe 100 percent in my life. I believe 100 percent in my journey."*

This is the first day of your dedication to something that will lead you into an awakening. Carry over these methods into day two and let them build upon each other. Especially if you're sick of worrying, start implementing these steps.

Summary

1. Question to start your day: *"What am I going to do today to believe in the power of my mind?"*
2. Do not watch or listen to any news. (Be very selective as to the news stories you read)
3. Tune into music and/or comedy
4. Smile inside your chest
5. Five minute meditation – become aware of your thoughts. *"I believe 100 percent in my ability to attract into my life everything that is right for me."*
6. At the end of your day declare: *"There is no danger in my belief. I believe 100 percent in my life. I believe 100 percent in my journey."*

Day Two

As you awaken in the morning take advantage of the window of a few seconds to a couple of minutes before the protective veil of the AB (automatic brain) descends. As you bask in the calm of these moments, ask yourself the question, *"What am I going to do today to believe in the power of my mind?"* Be aware that all too quickly, this calm signals vulnerability to your AB, automatically "reminding" it why you're supposed to feel unease and stress.

Creating this unease, in all likelihood, is one of three major saboteurs of your peace: money, health, and relationships. Money problems trigger the AB, and the AB in turn causes you to retreat from forward progress. Money is a tool of your automatic brain because you need money for food, clothing, and shelter—all essential for survival. Ill health naturally acts on the AB's danger triggers; but the AB doesn't have to wait for ill health. Even when we're feeling fine, it gets us to worry that we could get sick enough to die. Thirdly, relationships are an important source of AB scenarios in this way: The AB equates the threat of love that might be withdrawn with potential death and thus inability to pass along your DNA.

Allowing the thoughts of the AB to prevail just assures a constant state of confusion. Why? Because if you don't have enough money, say, the AB triggers over the obvious danger of poverty. But if you have a lot of money, it triggers for less obvious dangers related to fear of success. If you are sick the AB will trigger over the obvious danger that you could get worse. But even when you're healthy, it triggers over the fear that, as a patient said to me recently, "I'm afraid to be too happy because then something bad might happen." If you're not in a relationship, the lack of love is threatening, but when you are in a relationship, your AB triggers over its worry that the grass is greener on the other side—i.e., that other people's relationships are better than yours.

When you're beset with envy, keep in mind that even the very successful TV celebrity secretly wishes for what you have. The writer wishes he were a doctor; the doctor wishes she were a writer. The grass, in short, always seems greener. The real danger in following the AB, the part of our brain designed to "protect" us, is that the seesaw teeters up or down constantly. If you can manage to reject the ideas and direction of the AB, you will feel more balanced and stable. When you feel held down by the physical or mental power of the AB, repeat out loud or silently, *"I believe 100 percent in my life. I believe 100 percent in my journey."*

The AB's machinations are very effective at blocking your power to attract abundance. At any time of the day, unhelpful thoughts can creep into your mind to draw you away from optimism. When those thoughts are about money—maybe you're thinking about your shrinking net worth, or bills coming due, or whatever—intercept those thoughts with the affirmation: *"I believe 100 percent in my life. I believe 100 percent in my journey."* Then: *"I will always find a way and a way will always find me. I will always find money and money will always find me."* Repeat these over and over in your mind. It won't make your bills go away, but it will break through the blockade of the AB so you can unleash the power of your mind to attract what is right for you. The ideas and events that come to you *will* help you pay your bills, and also allow you not to be threatened by money – whether it is the abundance of it or the lack of it.

Health concerns are more great saboteurs. Whether you actually have current health problems or fear getting them, your AB uses the possibility of ill health to pull you back from a "dangerous" place. When that happens, it's time for the mantra: *"I will always find a way and a way will always find me. I will always find health and health will always find me."*

Relationships affect our thoughts and can gradually erode our belief. Our AB is constantly sizing up other people to see if they are a threat to us. This causes us, unconsciously or consciously, to jockey for position.

We learn to recognize those who are weaker than us and those who are stronger. But for today, Day Two on your path to belief, I want you to begin rejecting this reflex of the AB, and stop comparing yourself to anyone. Whether the comparison is well intentioned or not, the process serves only to strengthen your AB and push you further from belief. Do not compare your hair, your body, your house, your job, your wealth, your poverty, your spirituality, your intelligence—nothing.

Earlier in the book, I talked about Schadenfreude, the German term referring to one delighting in the hurt of another. We see this throughout our culture and often feel it in ourselves. It is part of human nature to feel envious of someone who we think has more than us. Many are familiar with the big fuss about the great swimmer Michael Phelps using a bong (marijuana paraphernalia). How did you feel about Bernard Madoff? Were you saddened for those who lost everything, or did you have a slight feeling of delight that those who had more than you are now suffering? Did you feel the same way toward Madoff himself? If you took pleasure from the troubles of these people, you can thank your AB. Don't beat yourself up about it, though. Just recognize that this brain always tries to keep us safe, and one way is by diminishing someone it senses is more powerful than us. Otherwise, thinks the AB, we might become subservient, to the point even of possible annihilation. To stop these kinds of feelings and thoughts, which eventually lead to brain drain, you don't want to feed that AB reflex. So, from today on, *avoid all exposure*—television, radio, news articles/reports—to anything that directly or indirectly fosters *delight in the hardship of another*. Sad to say, this means no more watching reality shows. Sorry!

Your AB, in cahoots with supporting evidence from your life memories, will throw at you every reason not to believe. Since the automatic brain is very good at this, you should avoid giving it any further help—it doesn't need help. Therefore, starting today, *avoid engaging negative people in conversation.* I am not saying you have to ignore them, but try not to prolong a conversation that turns negative. If you know people who perpetually wallow in doom and gloom, do not go out of your way to socialize with them. They represent a sort of "external" automatic brain, creating obstacles, which will challenge your belief.

The basic reaction of the AB is fight or flight. Perceived or real dangers trigger it, and you then fight or flee. Anger is the fight. Today, start becoming aware of situations that make you angry. This will help you perceive the dangers you are reacting to. Usually your AB thinks it's being one-upped by someone or something. When anger hits, it is very important to derail the physical response. Back off, start deep breathing (in through your nose, out through your mouth), and utter to yourself, *"There is no danger, there is no threat."* Anger *always* means your AB senses danger or threats. In other words, whenever there is anger, there is a danger trigger lurking.

For today's meditation exercise, find seven minutes for yourself during the day. Go to a quiet place, sit in a comfortable seat. Turn off your cell phone. Gently close your eyes. Listen and feel your breath flow in through your nose and out through your mouth. With your eyes still gently closed, picture yourself walking along a hallway toward an elevator. Feel the floor beneath your feet. Notice the texture of the walls. The hallway may be one familiar to you, or it may be one you imagine. As you approach the elevator, pause and focus again on your breath. Are you still breathing slowly, deliberately, deeply, in through your nose and out through your mouth? Feel the air flow in through your nostrils and then out through the back of your throat. Try not to blow the air out through pursed lips. Rather push it out slowly and evenly through the back of your throat with a gentle, windy *haaaaaaa* sound.

The more details you notice around you and the more completely you focus on your breathing, the less successful will be your AB's attempts to remove you from this very safe place, which it sees as vulnerable and dangerous. Continuing your very calm reverie, see the door of the elevator open. Step inside and observe the door closing behind you. Look around the elevator. Feel the floor beneath your feet. Look at the ceiling. You are alone here. And you are safe. Breathe slowly, always in through your nose and out through your mouth. Feel the peace. Do not believe any intruding thoughts, as insistent and hurtful though they may be. You are alone in your safe place. It is a place of your belief. You are insulated from danger. As you breathe, repeat in your mind, *"There is no danger, there is no threat. I am safe and I am free."* Let yourself finish the exercise when you are ready. It should take around seven minutes, give or take.

At the end of your day as you lie in bed, say in your mind, *"There is no danger in my belief. I believe 100 percent in my life. I believe 100 percent in my journey."*

Summing up

1. Question to start your day: *"What am I going to do today to believe in the power of my mind?"*

2. No matter what circumstance or thought triggers the AB, *"I believe 100 percent in my life. I believe 100 percent in my journey."* Then: *"I will always find a way and a way will always find me. [and for example] I will always find money and money will always find me."*

3. Do not compare yourself with anyone.

4. Avoid delighting in someone else's failure.

5. Avoid negative people and do not contribute to negative conversation.

6. When you get angry, back off, breathe, and think: *"There is no danger, there is no threat."*

7. Meditation—seven minutes, enter the elevator.

8. At bedtime: *As I lay down to sleep, there is no danger in my belief. I believe 100 percent in my life. I believe 100 percent in my journey."*

The end of Day Two is the beginning of your awakening—you are becoming more aware of the common triggers of your AB and the insidious way they have of diminishing your belief. Enjoy your new sense of awareness, insight, and self-knowledge. You're on the path to more self-control and to the flow of abundance that belief will create. Enjoy the freedom this knowledge bestows on you. You will see yourself moving away from the reflexive action of the AB and into the reflection of your mind, as it connects your body with spirit.

Day Three

By now you may be developing a better idea of what you should believe. After all, the name of this section is "Seven Days to Belief." The belief lies with your mind. Your mind is the portal to spirituality and thus the connection between you and a great ethereal energy. This energy forms the basis of inexplicable phenomena, as well as concepts like the law of attraction and karma. Believing in our mind rather than the mechanistic functioning of the automatic brain is the key to unleashing your repressed spirit.

The question with which you will begin today is, *"What am I going to do today to believe in the power of my mind?"*

Let's start coming up with answers. Although it seems as though the AB has its own mind, it does not. This is how it works: The AB **always** needs a trigger to get going. Information comes in through our five senses and hits the AB. Circumstances and situations (an amalgamation of data from the five senses) just *are*—they are not dangerous...that is, until referenced against our stored danger memories.

Memories are formed through life experience, mostly in childhood. When the data show up, if they match danger, the system sets off a chain reaction. Part of the reaction is physiologic effects, such as rapid heart rate or nervousness, and part is emotional effects, from thoughts. At this point your AB tries everything to remove you from the danger.

The thoughts come from the primitive portion of our brain's neocortex. They are just random thoughts that the AB uses to pull you from danger. They mean nothing except that they usually are strong enough to signal real danger. And even the physiologic reaction of the AB is enough to signal a danger, such as the fear of losing control or having a heart attack. All this is enough fuel to get you to fight or flee the initial "dangerous" situation picked up by your five senses. As I describe earlier on in the book, the initial danger for everyone is different, but the reaction of the AB is the same: a flurry of physical and emotional activity that further signals danger, thus creating a powerful urge to fight or flee whatever has sparked the response. Most people become disoriented by the barrage of activity from the AB. They start believing the thoughts it sends out. They start trusting the physical symptoms. Following the direction of the AB, they fight or flee the danger that triggered it.

The fact is, the AB needs a trigger. What are your triggers? What is your major trigger? Everyone has one or two major triggers. We get so used to the input from the AB that we don't even know what our triggers are. In spite of what you might think, money, health, and relationships are not the triggers. They are part of the internal information—the thoughts—that the AB generates to cause you to fight or flee your real trigger. They simply keep the pressure on until you successfully fight or flee your real trigger.

Earlier on, I explain how most people's AB equates the fear of losing love with death. I also show that merely becoming independent is a trigger, because when the brain is being formed as a child, it fears that leaving the "nest" could result in death. It may surprise you that abundance, having it all, is a major trigger both for those who do have it all and for those who don't. The reaction of the AB is fear, causing fight or flight. The idea of having it all triggers the AB's *flight* response, because one's abundance might mean losing the love of those who have less—perhaps parents or friends—or the *fight* response, leading to excess and decadence. For those struggling with weight issues, a major trigger could be thinness, or being fit, especially for anyone who grew up in a household where being thin meant you were different and therefore less likely to be accepted and given love. Leaving the familiar environment of the nest means venturing into unchartered territory. The unknown is always a danger trigger to the AB. Those who are obese as adults may have had this as a familiar environment while growing up. Those who constantly struggle with finances may have had a familiar environment while growing up where money was always a struggle and those who had money were often ridiculed. Thus a fit body (i.e. the unfamiliar, locked into the AB's memory banks) becomes a danger trigger as does having financial security (i.e. the unfamiliar, locked into the AB's memory banks).

The question is, what are you going to believe? Are you going to keep believing the endless drama of the AB, triggered by dangers that aren't really dangerous? Once you identify your triggers, you can scorn the predictable nature of the AB and stop believing the illogical thoughts it generates.

Today, on Day Three of the path to believing, work on identifying your danger triggers. We've already touched on some of the universal ones: being independent, change (moving into the unfamiliar), losing love, being one-upped, vulnerability, death. Others may be more personal—for example, being thin, or healthy, or physically fit, becoming intimate, staying monogamous, happiness, financial wealth, or maybe just being the best you can be. So on this day, identify three of your danger triggers. I'm a doctor; should I feel that it's dangerous to be seen outside my white coat (being vulnerable, having a narrow definition of myself)? Do you find yourself without a job for the first time in your adult life? Think back to what life was like when you were growing up. It doesn't matter how old or young you are now. Were conditions placed upon you to receive love? For example, were you told not to speak out of turn? Were you ridiculed about your body? Any circumstance as a child that implied you would not receive love unless you met certain conditions may turn up now, in adulthood, as a trigger to your AB.

In the first chapter, I wrote about the development of our modern mind at around the time of Biblical creation. This mind is our connection to the spiritual world and resides in the most recent part of our neocortex.

It is the structure that allows you and me to step outside our automatic brain and observe its workings. It cannot be influenced by the AB, but its workings can trigger the AB and it may well represent the supreme danger trigger for the AB. Thoughts generated in our mind conflict with the notion that we are mortal and bound by the limits of our physical, sensory world. That is the notion upon which the AB has evolved to rely. Continued trust in your AB, therefore, blocks authentic belief in your thinking mind and in something greater than our physical world. Belief in the ability of your mind will not only help you navigate the obstacles of this physical world, but will give you a deeper sense of belonging to something larger. That is the belief that I seek and that I hope you seek as well.

Today you will practice observing the AB with your mind. For example, if you have identified being one-upped by someone as a major trigger, watch what happens when you are in a situation where that happens: Perhaps you are cut off on the road, or your spouse says something you feel is insulting, or the person in front of you at the bakery snatched up the last Babka. Observe your initial reaction and then watch your thoughts. You'll probably go through a chain of events whose purpose is to cause you to fight or flee the individual who is one-upping you. The fight might be anger; the flight, an internalized feeling of stress, withdrawal, or avoidance.

Our mind is there to bring into our life that which is right for us. The AB just spins its wheels; the more we believe in it, the more we buy into the lies it uses to protect us from things from which we need no protection. Just step back and watch it.

Your thinking mind has been with you your entire life. But it might have been staying in the background if, for your entire life, you have been believing, trusting, and taking direction from the protective machinery of the AB.

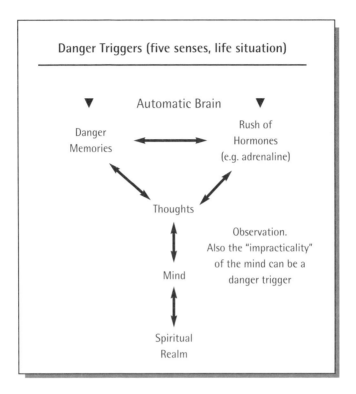

Through meditation you can begin to coax your mind out of the background. Let's continue the meditation exercise from Day Two. Your eyes are gently closed. Return to the elevator following the steps from yesterday. As the doors close, hear your breath—in through the nose, out through the mouth. Stand in the elevator and feel the warmth. *"I am safe, I am free."* As you inhale, begin to picture in your mind a way you have always wished you could be. For instance, if you've wanted to be more physically fit, picture yourself as a fit person. See that person with your mind's eye. As you look at that person, do you feel yourself getting anxious? If you do, that is your AB, and you have identified a major trigger. How about being healthy without any ailments or thoughts of being sick? How about being happy? Picture yourself happy and secure, having it all—financial wealth, health, and a joyful relationship and perhaps family. Are you getting a little anxious? As you breathe slowly in through your nose and out through your mouth, watch this person that is you. The images in your mind's eye can trigger the AB, but you do not have to believe the result, no matter how uncomfortable it may be. Continue to breathe. The meditation today will last about 12 minutes, give or take.

Your breath is fuel for your mind. Our mind is the foundation of our belief. It is the liaison between the customary workings of the AB and the supernatural essence of spirit. Develop it, learn to believe, trust, and take direction from it, and then you will understand what belief truly is.

When ready for bed, declare, *"There is no danger in my belief. I believe 100 percent in my life. I believe 100 percent in my journey."*

Summing Up:

1. Question to start your day: *"What am I going to do today to believe in the power of my mind?"*
2. Identify three major danger triggers.
3. Step back, in your mind, and familiarize yourself with the physical and emotional reactions and thoughts generated by the AB when triggered.
4. Stop believing, trusting, or taking direction from these thoughts.
5. Meditation—about 12 minutes; watch yourself with your mind's eye.
6. At bedtime: *"There is no danger in my belief. I believe 100 percent in my life. I believe 100 percent in my journey."*

Day Four

Your mind is the link between your needs and wants and a more meaningful spiritual belonging. Truly believing in your mind is the foundation of belief in phenomena we cannot explain. However, the incessant presence of the automatic brain stifles the work of our mind. Keeping one's belief up is the cornerstone of my seven-day program. Belief comes and goes throughout our lives. The AB is the reason for our endless need to prove our belief. In Chapter 19, I explained how despite the apparent miracles bestowed upon the Israelites during their exodus from Egypt, they quickly gave up their belief and abandoned Moses in favor of a golden calf.

To start your day ask, *"What will I do today to believe in the power of my mind?"*

For thousands of years, people have struggled with the automatic brain and thus had great difficulty keeping their thoughts from drifting into the future or the past in order to keep them safe. This pattern is illustrated by a quote from Proverbs: *Today is the tomorrow that you worried about yesterday.* In the book of Exodus, Lot's wife turned into a pillar of salt for looking back to the burning Sodom and Gomorrah, apparently the price of longing for the past. Albert Einstein once said, "The distinction between past, present, and future is merely an illusion, albeit a stubborn one."

In order to develop and maintain belief, you must reject the automatic tendency of the AB to look to the past and future for today's decisions and behavior. The AB appears to be logical—it taps into your five senses and things you know, and bases its predictions on statistics and probabilities. So you believe, trust, and take direction from your AB as it rejects the fantasies of your mind—like the law of attraction and karma. But—guess what—your AB does not know everything. A few hundred years ago, everyone was sure the earth was flat. We have just begun to tap into our understanding of our mind and its abilities. Your mind is a gift and, when allowed, will draw to you everything that is right for you.

The information the AB uses to deal with today's challenges is not real. Most of your past is stored in memories that are inaccurate and do not match today's reality. But that doesn't stop the AB from extrapolating those memories into the future in a pathetic attempt to make known the unknown. Anything it conjures up about the future is nothing more than fantasy. The past predicts the present or the future only if you believe it will.

If the past had been exactly the way you wished, do you know what your life would look like today? If everything had gone as you imagined it should have, would you even be alive today? What if you did what you think you should have 20 years ago, and made a right turn down Main Street instead of a left on Elm Street? Who knows what would have been there to greet you, or whose paths you would have crossed?

The past is an illusion we reflexively drift to for affirmation of the present. Believing, trusting, or taking direction from the past as predictor of the future shows that your automatic brain is trying to keep you out of danger—so it's something to avoid.

Today, Day Four, you will begin focusing on your daily activities. Your AB decides whether the past is good or bad, but your mind can override this thinking and you can decide whether to believe it or not. Tomorrow will eventually be today. You can let your AB lead you into the future before it comes, thus influencing any outcome, or you can focus on today, with no distraction into the fantasy of future unknowns. Beginning today, realize that your mind is with you now and stays with you always. Reject thoughts about the past if they cause anxiety or sadness, as those are signs your AB is working to get you to fight or flee, respectively, a current danger. Reject projections of the future as nothing more than fantasies—a misguided attempt to help you be better prepared. You may find the following affirmation helpful: *"Belief in today makes tomorrow complete and yesterday obsolete."*

A method I have found very useful in cultivating belief in today, and hence the power of my mind, is a Daily Magic journal, as described in Chapter 19. Ordinary circumstances can go a long way to instilling belief when you recognize that certain decisions, choices, and experiences lead to other quite remarkable things, no matter how negative they may seem at first.

In Chapter 19, I told a seemingly trivial tale of a set of keys slipping out of my shorts pocket and settling under the cushion of the couch where I lay while watching a ballgame on a long-ago warm summer afternoon. That evening, I needed those keys to go out. I retraced my steps and found the keys. That's it—nothing spiritual or cosmic, just a set of car keys that fell out of my pocket while I watched a ballgame.

My keys were slipping out of my pocket, below my level of awareness. It made me wonder what else might be happening very close to us, or within us, that is escaping our awareness. The AB relies completely on our five senses to determine what is real, but the reality is that for most of us, we recognize only a small portion of the input from those senses. In medical school, I watched film clips of Himalayan monks controlling their body temperature and respirations entirely by focus, awareness, and willpower. Focus, awareness, and willpower are the work of your mind, and there are ways of fostering that.

Last year on January 23, I made an entry in my Daily Magic journal. I described a concert at my son's middle school at which the chorus sang "Starry Starry Night" by Don McLean. For me, it was a particularly moving rendition. The conductor explained that the song was based on the life and suicidal death of the artist Vincent Van Gogh. Fast-forward to New Year's Day 2009. Our family has a New Year's ritual of watching the

Twilight Zone Marathon on the Sci Fi network. The TV where I exercise did not get this channel, so while channel-surfing I found a PBS special on Wayne Dyer. I enjoyed his presentation and it helped me through my first workout of the year. About three hours later, during a commercial break from the Twilight Zone, I decided to see if he was still on. Sure enough, he was on and began talking about things that inspire us. He said (paraphrasing), "we get inspiration from many areas in our life—people we meet, books we read, movies we see' music we hear. I got inspiration from a musician named Don McLean. You know him—'Bye, Bye Miss American Pie' (audience started clapping and singing along)…No, that's not the one. He wrote and performed a song, a very moving, inspirational song for me, about Vincent Van Gogh, 'Starry, Starry Night'…" At that moment, I felt a particular empathy, a synchronicity if you will, with Dr. Dyer. More importantly, I recognized how important a seemingly simple circumstance a year earlier could be for my belief.

One night, my pager awakened me three times—at 11:30 p.m., 12:05 a.m., and finally at 5:25 a.m. The calls were non-emergency calls from a lab, and went through because of a miscommunication directing them *not* to call me. I must admit these calls, especially the last one, triggered my AB! When I got to the office in the morning, I shared with my staff the events of the night/morning before, while a patient filled out her physical-exam paperwork in the waiting area.

In the exam room, I rehashed the events with my patient. The conversation somehow led to a discussion about events surrounding the death of her husband some 15 years earlier. She and her husband had argued a week before his death—he was protesting the fact that the responsibility for replacing the light bulbs in their home fell entirely on his shoulders. Then he died, and about a day later, all the lights in her house went out! I share this story because if it had not been for my late-night experience, we likely would never have had this conversation, and would never have had our discussion about her husband. I have had many conversations with this patient during the 15 years I've known her, but this was the first time the conversation took this kind of turn. This type of "supernatural" event strengthens my belief in things that our AB cannot explain. Just think how many unnoticed events go by in your life that could advance your belief.

If you haven't already, today, on Day Four, begin keeping a Daily Magic journal. Entries can be anything you choose, but especially those circumstances that deviate from your normal routine. Do not try to figure out what the circumstances might mean. For example, I may go to the hospital in the morning or early afternoon instead of my usual routine of going after office hours. Everything I experience, then, will be something unexpected. In my journal I might write that I made rounds earlier and bumped into Dr. Smith or saw someone I had not seen in a long time. Everything I experience will happen simply because of some deviation in my normal pattern.

You may lose your cell phone today, or the stock you invested in could suddenly plummet on the day you bought it. Circumstances may occur that seem bad. You should write them down if they are unexpected. They all connect to something larger. Do not try to figure it all out. If it were not for that monster of a spouse from whom you divorced, you would not now have the child without whom you could not imagine your life. Write the circumstances down and see how they enhance your belief in the power of your mind. Do not let yourself believe they are bad. They just *are*. They just are circumstance. Allow them to stand alone. Their significance may or may not ever reveal itself. It does not matter. There will be enough connection to reaffirm your belief as long as you temper the AB's insatiable need for evidence to prove it wrong.

Today's meditation exercise starts where you left off in the elevator on Day Three. But today you will not visualize the situation in which you wish to be. Instead, as you sit in your comfortable seat, begin your relaxation before you descend. Curl your toes; as you exhale, relax your toes. As you inhale, tighten your calf muscles; as you exhale, relax them. Continue this exercise from your feet to the top of your head (lifting your eyebrows is a way to contract the top part of your head). Throughout this exercise, see yourself smiling broadly. Do not actually smile broadly until you are to contract your facial muscles. Once you have reached this point, allow your facial muscles to settle where your mind's eye directs (if someone were to observe you, they would see a soft smile upon your face). After you finish this part of the meditation, on Day Five you will be ready to descend in the elevator. I have chosen descent, as it will take you deep within yourself.

The key to belief lies deep within you, and it comes before you can believe in God. Do not ask God to do things for you, believe that your mind, God's gift to you, has the power to create and do the things that you have previously attributed to God. By doing so, your belief becomes much more solid. It withstands the usual waning that occurs after religious services or listening to someone particularly motivating or spiritual. Yes, believing in the power of your mind can reaffirm your relationship with your God and help you to develop a solid belief in something greater than your mind can comprehend. Believing in the power of the mind, though, does not require you believe in God. Your belief will lead you to experience something much greater than the limitations of your AB and you can call it what you will. The important feature is 100 percent belief and unshakable faith in the existence of a power that is much larger than our five senses can comprehend and capable of bringing to you everything that is right for your life.

Ending your day, declare: *"There is no danger in my belief. I believe 100 percent in my life. I believe 100 percent in my journey."*

Summing Up:

1. Question to start the day: *"What will I do today to believe in the power of my mind?"*

2. Observe the tendency of your AB to drift into thoughts about the past and future, and remember the proverb, *Today is the tomorrow that you worried about yesterday.*

3. To keep focused on today, use the affirmation when your brain wanders: *Belief in today makes tomorrow complete and yesterday obsolete.*

4. Begin keeping a Daily Magic journal.

5. Meditation—Relaxation before your descent. Smile broadly inside. Belief in your mind's power lies within.

6. At bedtime: *"There is no danger in my belief. I believe 100 percent in my life. I believe 100 percent in my journey."*

Day Five

Day Five starts with the question: *"What will I do today to believe in the power of my mind?"* And you will begin to think, "What is it about this belief that is so hard?" I hope that as you go through my seven day program, there will be times that you feel something click and you begin to believe in your inherent power. Maybe you feel a moment of calmness, optimism, possibility. This feeling may be relatively short-lived, perhaps lasting just a few minutes or maybe even a couple of days—until the AB once again provides proof that your belief is fantasy, childish, impractical. In fact, our trust in our AB never seems to need any proof—it is our default belief, it is automatic. Belief in the power of our mind is not automatic, and needs continual proof. That is what I look to change.

Today on Day Five, it is time to see that the apparent realities of our automatic brain that define our personal reality are in fact less real than belief in the power of the mind, which explains phenomena like the law of attraction and karma.

To review briefly: The automatic brain is the primitive part of our brain that responds to danger by protecting us, ultimately ensuring our survival or that of our DNA, through our children. What one person's AB interprets as danger is different from another's, but the reaction is always the same, fight or flight. Danger is the 'On' switch, the trigger, and the response is to fight or flee that danger. It really is as simple as that. There is always a danger trigger to explain aggressiveness (fight), passivity (flight), anger (fight), anxiety (fight or flight), or depression (fight or flight). The complicated part of this is understanding what the dangers are, where they come from, and how our AB exaggerates by generating manipulative, seductive, and untruthful thoughts. I have urged you never to take direction from your AB, because it always exaggerates to protect you from the worst-case scenario. Recognizing that exaggeration and shifting your belief to the invincible truth and power of the mind prepares you for any real threat. More importantly, it will allow you to attract into your life those things that are generally considered marks of success—money, health, strong relationships, peace of mind.

Many people who read my work have no trouble recognizing the workings of the AB in others, but don't notice that they still believe, trust, and take direction from their own AB. It is essential to see that the "realities" of your life as directed by your AB are not real at all.

Although the automatic brain uses its own version of logic and reason to persuade us to withdraw into a safe area, it relies on thoughts, not tangible events. Those thoughts come mostly from childhood connections formed in the AB as its danger memories—its data and proof. We have no way of knowing what our life would look like if the woulda, coulda, shouldas of the past actually happened. Furthermore, the future is merely conjured-up fantasy.

We believe our AB because of the apparent logic, probability, and accuracy of our five senses, from which it derives its influence. The problem with this is that our five senses can't hope to process the enormity of our true reality. What is this reality? Here are the facts: We are 65 percent water (about the same as many other animals), and, like everything else in the universe, we're made up of atoms—in fact, more atoms than there are stars in the universe (by some expert accounts). While I'm on a roll, the atom has a nucleus with electrons orbiting around it. Picture a fly on the turf of Houston's Astrodome—that's the nucleus. Go to the farthest point in the nose-bleed section of the stands, and that is where the electrons are. And between the nucleus and electrons is NOTHING. We, in reality, are mostly empty space. But we're also energy and the power of our mind derives from that energy. Here's a relevant affirmation: *I am energy; my mind is powerful.* The nothing that exists between nucleus and electrons is energy.

How does this relate

How does this relate to your daily life? Belief in the power of your mind means rejecting the automatic thoughts and direction of the AB. The above realities can empower you to do this. Showing yourself the fallacies of the AB in your life is important, and today—on Day Five—you should construct your first revelation grid.

Many patients have expressed to me their frustration with obsessive worrying. Any undesirable behavior is *always* preceded by a danger trigger. For many, *not* worrying is the danger trigger. A childhood household culture of worrying is a powerful breeding ground for a danger memory in adulthood. The contorted reasoning of the AB is that somehow a person will be punished for not worrying. The overly dramatic AB equates loss of love with death. In a childhood culture of worry, you risk losing love if you appear cold, uncompassionate, and free from worry; in other words, different from the others in the household. That is the power of the danger memory—the automatic brain narrowing reality. (Being different from your parents has a strong impact on your developing AB. This shows up in many other areas, such as weight control and substance abuse.)

Here's an example of a revelation grid from Gloria in Chapter 11:

Circumstance/Trigger	Danger	Comfort/Safety
Worry	*(Box #1) Feel lousy all the time; feel stressed; wreck my health; loss of quality of life; alive but not really living.*	*(Box #2)* I know I'm doing everything I can to prevent the disaster; showing myself that I love my kids.
Not worrying	*(Box #3)* Harm will come to pass; caught off guard; I will not have prepared or prevented it; disaster is certain; kids will be in danger	*(Box #4) Living out of comfort zone in a place of serenity, where all is well and peaceful; I am at the top of my game mentally; I'm sharp and unafraid; no limit at my chances for success; I'm enjoying my family, because we have such a good time, my kids and I, when I let go of this stuff!*

If you build your own revelation grid, it helps to know that the actual danger (or trigger) is the opposite of your present behavior. In the above example, Gloria's present behavior is worrying. She continues to worry because *not* to worry is a danger to her AB. If you eat without limits and have an unfit body, the opposite—eating with restrictions, being fit and trim—might be your danger. If you are chronically unhappy and pessimistic, your AB sees being happy and optimistic as dangerous or threatening. When you construct your grid, you should get a glimpse into your mind: it will be in box #4. The previous days' exercises and the above realities should help keep you from making box #4 yet another danger trigger to your AB. Believing, trusting, and taking direction from what you come up with is unleashing the power of your mind. It will truly set you free.

Although I have been saving the meditation exercises for the end of each daily entry, I personally meditate first thing in the morning after my shower. I suggest you set aside a period of about 15 or 20 minutes. Your AB will challenge you: "What, are you crazy? I don't have 15 or 20 minutes to spare in my day!" If lack of time is a danger to you, create a grid that labels "having enough time" as your danger. See what you come up with. Believing in the power of your mind and making time for meditation will always create enough time for everything you need and want.

For example, here is a recent revelation grid completed my patient when he responded that he is too busy and had no time for meditation.

Circumstance/Trigger	Danger	Comfort/Safety
No Time, Too Busy	*(Box #1) Over-stressed, ultimately leading to disease*	*(Box #2) Sense that things aren't falling through the cracks; taking care of what needs to be taken care of; taking care of obligations.*
Taking time, having time	*(Box #3) Business will suffer Things that need to get done, won't*	*(Box #4) Peace, relaxation. More energy. More healthy (more time to figure out how to make better use of my time)*

What will it take to make this patient and all others **believe** in Box 4 and believe that there is no danger in taking time. The answers lie within *Seven Days to Belief*.

Start your meditation from the beginning as I explained for previous days—the elevator scenario. After relaxing your muscles, continue with deep, slow inhaling through your nose and exhaling through your mouth. Picture in your mind's eye the floor numbers from 1 to 5 on the control panel of the elevator. Start on the ground level floor. (for those of you who feel your AB will be robustly activated by descending below ground level, I suggest you start at the fifth floor and descend 4, 3,2,1, ground). With each breath in and out, picture the next-lower floor number lighting as if you were really in an elevator. Feel yourself lower to descending levels. Continue until you reach the fifth floor. For today, that will finish your descent. Continue your breathing and feel yourself reversing direction and rising back up to the ground level (or to the fifth floor if that's where you started). This will end today's meditation.

At bedtime: *"There is no danger in my belief. I believe 100 percent in my life. I believe 100 percent in my journey."*

Summing up:

1. Question to start the day: *"What will I do today to believe in the power of my mind?"*
2. There is always a danger trigger to explain aggressiveness, passivity, anger, anxiety, or depression.
3. The fallacies of the past and future.
4. The reality that we are mostly energy

5. Our inherent energy is the power of our mind—*I am energy; my mind is powerful.*

6. Revelation grid to recognize your dangers and expose the falsehoods of your AB.

7. Meditation—Descend five levels.

8. At bedtime: *"There is no danger in my belief. I believe 100 percent in my life. I believe 100 percent in my journey."*

Day Six

You've been working for many years, and all you have to show for it is a shrinking nest egg or a paltry Social Security or pension check. Or maybe you're still working, and you're getting increasingly nervous about your job security and whether you can make enough to pay your debts. You pass people in the street and see the somber faces, the store-closing signs, and you wonder, is this all there is?

As your days progress, those kind of thoughts and events will challenge your belief. Make no mistake: The challenge comes from the powerful action of the automatic brain. As I wrote in Day Five, the AB always requires a trigger, and world and life events such as collapsing financial markets and skyrocketing unemployment can serve as an obvious trigger. Once the AB is activated, the fight-or-flight reaction shows up in the form of stress, anger, nervousness, sadness, anxiety, and depression, among other feelings and emotions. The thoughts and physical symptoms that follow directly challenge belief and can place you in protective lock-down mode. That mode prevents you from seeing anything beyond what your AB directs you to believe.

As we develop our belief in the power of our mind, it is important each day to remind ourselves that there is something beyond the limited reference point of the AB. That something is a greater force—a life force—that exists within us, that supersedes the false logic of the AB; a force and reality that beckon us to believe in it. It is the essence of who we are. It is our mind, and our mind represents a force unlike any the AB can muster. Your mind can help you break through the safety net, the box, the veil that your AB wants you to believe is the only way to protect yourself from danger and keep you safe.

The AB creates a protective shell, with a narrow definition of yourself (for example, "I am a nervous person," or "I am never happy," or "I am an unlucky person.") that prevents you from seeing beyond it. If you recently lost your job, you may be having difficulty seeing yourself doing anything else; because you have defined yourself in a certain role. Now that the role has changed, the fear of "re-defining" yourself is paralyzing. Make no mistake that paralysis stems from the activity of your automatic brain. Do not believe, trust, or take direction from thoughts that indicate you are incapable of doing something else.

Another example of a negative definition is a medical illness. Christopher is a patient with prostate cancer who went to his one and only support group. Although the men in the group were "a great bunch of guys," they seemed to define themselves by their illness. He wants to go ahead and enjoy his life, not denying the fact that he has prostate cancer, but as a man who defines himself first as a lover of life, and secondarily as a man who just so happens to have prostate cancer. Not, "I have prostate cancer and I will now try to enjoy life." It's hard to love life when you define yourself first as being sick. When he is enjoying an activity with his family and the thought shoots into his head (from his AB), reminding him that he has prostate cancer, Christopher is able to affirm, "Yes, I am loving my life and having a great time with my family. Oh yes, and I have prostate cancer, as well." This enables him not to believe thoughts generated by the AB. Thoughts as, "What are you wasting time with your family, you better act now, you have no time to spare." Such is the deception of our automatic brain. By rejecting the intrusions of his AB, with a clearer mind, Christopher will be able to approach is illness more sensibly while still enjoying life.

Today, Day Six, to cultivate your belief in the power of your mind, you will begin to see beyond the protective veneer of the automatic brain.

You will start your day in the usual way, with a question: *"What will I do today to believe in the power of my mind?"*

With the activation of the AB, we see ourselves scrambling, overwhelmed, looking for some way out. That places us further into the doom-and-gloom cage, the result of our AB's always preparing us for the worst-case scenario. As I have said before, you cannot believe, trust, or take direction from *anything* the AB throws your way. It will never steer you right even though now and then you may think it does. As in the over-protective-parent example I described in earlier chapters, the seduction of listening to such sources is that they actually *are* right some of the time.

Since the AB uses input from the five senses as ammunition for its protection of your physical body, I suggest you take a look at what's right in front of you. The AB is programmed to prepare for the worst-case scenario and to position you above other people to increase your chance for survival. By this logic, what you don't have and what someone else has could place you in a "dangerous" position. So the AB has you wishing and looking for what you don't have instead of seeing what is right under your nose. What you don't know can hurt you, according to the logic of the AB. To recognize the power of your mind and begin to activate it, you must become familiar with those things that you do know and be happy, secure, and grateful for that which you already have. All of that can form a strong bond with the power of your mind.

Start right away when you first awaken. Take advantage of the first few seconds or minutes before your AB begins warning you of the dangers of today. After you ask yourself the daily question, pause for a moment with closed eyes. What do you hear? Listen. Hear something that you usually don't hear (birds outside, perhaps). Turn your attention to touch.

What do you feel touching your body? Feel something that you ordinarily wouldn't notice. Now open your eyes. Look at your surroundings. Notice something that is always there but that you never see. Maybe it is a CD case that has been on your dresser for months. Or maybe it is a book on your nightstand that you left there weeks ago with the intention of reading. There are things in your field of vision that you glance over everyday but do not really see. Today, allow them to register; recognize them, see them.

As you step into the shower, feel the water on your skin. Listen to the water as it skips off the tiles. I bet your AB is racing so much there are some days you don't even remember being in the shower! As the day progresses, remember to smell. What do you smell? During your day, when you eat, slow down and really savor what you are eating. Can you distinguish the different tastes of ingredients in the soup or sandwich or salad you are eating? Before getting into your car, take two deep breaths and look at the sky or the horizon; notice something that you normally do not see. If you think everything you routinely see, hear, taste, smell, or feel defines your reality, be aware that you may be missing most of it by relying on incomplete information to guide you.

Your AB is firing constantly these days and will prevent you from seeing anything that does not feed its immediate purpose—to protect you. However, when you listen to its direction you will continue to bounce back and forth without real protection. For example, your AB will persuade you that you cannot afford to take any leisure time for exercise because you need to spend all your time figuring a way out of your present financial situation. When you listen to this direction for awhile and both your physical and financial health have gotten worse, your AB directs you to relax more and exercise so you don't get a heart attack. So you do that, and then you are back to where you started, and the cycle starts again.

Another common instruction from the AB is to avoid anything that makes you feel vulnerable. Example: stepping out of any previously defined role. One of the greatest ironies I have learned through life is that vulnerability is often my greatest asset. Becoming more than the narrow definition of a traditional doctor has opened doors for me—and has brought me a deeper understanding of myself and my life's purpose, along with greater respect from my patients. The AB constantly warns against exposure to vulnerability, but the more you expand the limits of your AB-imposed comfort zone, the more your life opens up.

Before you greet the world, your AB may direct you to make sure every hair on your head is in place, or to check yourself in the mirror a million times before going out to a party. Allowing yourself to be less than perfect brings you a confident swagger that is more attractive than any makeup or fancy clothes. If you listen to the circular logic of the AB, you'll never see the true beauty in your world, in your life. And you'll go on making the same bad decisions and reacting the same counterproductive ways. Use the affirmation, *"Vulnerability is my greatest asset,"* and see how things begin to change.

Although your AB feels you cannot spare a second of time away from the doom and gloom of your financial situation, you must find time. Over the weekend, get outside to see the things in nature you have long stopped noticing. You need to practice seeing beyond the restrictive boundaries of the AB's protective box.

Unlike our AB, the mind is nonjudgmental. We all judge, and the automatic judgments we make are yet another example of how our AB operates to protect us. How many times have you been in a public place—a supermarket, say—and you find yourself assessing how everyone you pass is dressed. And then you move on to what their lives must be like. The thoughts move along automatically.

What do you think about when you see someone driving a fancy, expensive car? What goes through your mind if the driver cuts you off? What if you attend an affair with people who you think have more or less than you? We seem unable to stop constantly sizing people up. This instinct may protect us from potential violators of our space, but, as with the other actions of our AB, has little to do with reality. So much is going through our brains when we encounter someone new that we do not recognize his or her real essence. We rarely really listen to what people are saying in conversation. Our judgments serve only to feed our AB, to insulate us from danger, to help us jockey for position.

If all of this sounds pretty dismal, keep in mind that while you are forming those hasty judgments about people you encounter, they too are having thoughts about you, as they too have an AB that's attempting to shield them. Reflexive judgments come from the automatic brain; *reflective* judgments come from our mind. The trick is to distinguish between what's reflexive and what's reflective. The reflective part of your mind evaluates your five senses' input to determine whether there's a *need* for protection. That part is easy, as there are few circumstances in our everyday lives where we really need to be protective. The reflective process is, in a way, a matter of taking a step back from yourself and evaluating the types of judgments you are making. That is the power of your mind and its direction is that which you want to follow.

What happens if instead of being reflective we act on reflexive judgments? For one thing, we look for others to share and validate our judgments, giving rise to gossip, and providing fodder for the AB. The reality is that we have plenty to keep us busy just sorting out our own thoughts, so dwelling on the judgments of others serves only to cloud our mind's vision.

The thoughts that creep into your brain about other people tell you less about those people than they do about yourself. Your judgments can help you expose the types of thoughts that keep you listening to your AB.

Understand that most judgments of others are just your AB's attempt to empower you and to give you a sense of being better than the person you judge. Recognize that you might secretly wish someone you consider better than you—someone you envy—could be brought down to your level or lower.

Although your AB wants you to believe that judgment of others is necessary for your protection, it is just another part of the AB you must avoid completely. Your reflective mind will let you react quickly enough if the situation calls for immediate judgment. All the constant background judgment serves only to insulate you more from your mind.

Today's meditation exercise brings you closer to your inner guidance and trumps anything the AB can come to offer.

Start your meditation from the beginning as I explained for previous days—the elevator scenario. After relaxing your muscles, continue with deep, slow inhaling through your nose and exhaling through your mouth. Picture in your mind's eye the floor numbers from 1 to 10 on the control panel of the elevator. Start on the ground level floor. (For those of you who feel your AB will be protectively activated by descending below ground level, I suggest you start at the tenth floor and descend through 9, 8, 7, 6, 5, 4, 3, 2, 1 to the ground floor.) With each breath in and out, picture the next-lower floor number lighting as if you were really in an elevator. Feel yourself descend to lower levels. Continue until you reach the 10th underground floor (or ground level).

For today, stay in this position for as many breaths as you choose. Face the closed doors as you begin to breathe slowly in through your nose and out through your mouth, or if you so choose, out through your nose—slow and steady. When you feel ready, continue to breathe in this fashion and watch the *ascending* numbers as you reverse direction and rise back up to the ground level (or to the tenth floor if that's where you started). This will be the end of today's meditation. You are now prepared for the seventh day—the day you come face to face with your mind.

At bedtime: *"There is no danger in my belief. I believe 100 percent in my life. I believe 100 percent in my journey."*

Summing up:

1. Question to start the day: *"What will I do today to believe in the power of my mind?"*
2. Avoid narrow definitions of yourself
3. Do not believe, trust, or take direction from the reflexive actions and thoughts your AB generates, but instead the reflective thoughts and actions of your mind.
4. See, hear, touch, smell, taste what you usually do not appreciate. Get outside in nature.
5. Exercise gratitude and focus upon what you have.
6. *Vulnerability is my greatest asset*
7. Adopt a nonjudgmental attitude.
8. Meditation—Descend ten levels.
9. At bedtime: *"There is no danger in my belief. I believe 100 percent in my life. I believe 100 percent in my journey."*

As you develop your belief in the power of your mind, you will find that its reflective nature will become a reflex in and of itself—your default reflex (as when one plays music without listening to the blocking thoughts of the AB, just playing). Thus, the habitual control of your AB will gradually fade, exposing you to a more peaceful and successful life.

Day Seven

Today is Day Seven on your road to belief. When you awaken in the morning, pause for a moment and take a deep breath, in through your nose and out through your mouth. Then ask yourself today's question: *"What will I do today to believe in the power of my mind?"*

I will guess that throughout the week you have tried a few of my suggestions for Days One through Six. I will further guess that as the meditation exercise grew deeper and more complicated, you decided to skip those parts of the seven-day plan. Now, when Day Seven is upon you, you may find yourself wondering, "Is that all there is?" Your belief in something greater than your tangible environment and life experiences still wavers. You may go to your place of worship weekly and feel inspired for a few hours, only to come up against the usual challenges and watch your belief dwindle.

The most important component of my seven-day plan is meditation—the most sure fire way to stop brain drain. As I have mentioned numerous times in this book and shared with many of my readers and patients, everything I write stems from my life experience. My insights come from the personal sabotages of my (and others') automatic brain and triumphs of the mind. I have shared with you how I listened to the voice of my inner guide, whom I call Abe, while taking a linear algebra exam as a freshman in college. I later encountered my inner sage while meditating.

I share my experiences with "Abe" knowing that others' automatic brains might dismiss me as a psychotic and irrational dreamer. It doesn't worry me. Through continual meditation, Abe has guided me to a belief system that is quite compatible with the "real" world. My beliefs override the negativity and worst-case scenarios with which my automatic brain constantly bombards me. The success I enjoy is solely because I do not follow my automatic brain. As I strive to reject its fear-based nature, I see myself growing beyond anything I could have ever imagined.

It's likely that your automatic brain does not want you to meditate. Doing so, to the AB, places you in a dangerous, unknown territory. From tens of thousands of years of development, the AB instinctively activates to put up your guard when you're resting, sleeping, or relaxing; because those states can leave you vulnerable to attack. In meditation, as with so many other worthwhile things in life, the path is not always easy to your higher mind.

There is no greater technique to foster belief in the power of your mind than meditation. It is for this reason that I devote this final day of my plan to only one activity—meditation.

Your meditation will be unique to you. I have suggested the beginning steps of a meditation, but your personal meditation does not have to meet any other person's description, including mine. You do not have to act like or become a yogi or say "om" in the way you may have seen done by people practicing transcendental meditation. You should not attach any expectations to your meditation but should do this exercise not looking for anything. Your meditation is the vehicle to come face to face with your higher mind—the portal to your spirituality, and hence your belief in the power of *your* mind, in yourself. It is not something you have to look for; it is always there. Meditation will connect you to your true self, a place without judgment or guilt. It is not a competition, and you are not trying to be the best at meditating. You simply exist in your meditation, suspended in time and space.

Keep these points in mind for your meditation:
– You must accept fully that this exercise poses no danger or threat: no danger of attack while in your meditation, no danger of being ridiculed by someone, no danger from productive time lost, and

no threat to spiritual or even agnostic/atheist belief you already hold.

– Understand that negative thoughts about this practice rise only as a fabrication of your AB. They are simply a reflex to the "danger" posed by this exercise.

– For some, meditation may serve as your daily prayer. If you believe you are connecting to God through your meditation, avoid asking for specific things. If you ask for anything, ask that this higher force help you believe in your individual abilities; believe in the power of your mind.

– Breathing is of paramount importance. We go through our lives breathing, but we are not really providing optimal amounts of the most vital nutrient to our body—oxygen. I have done many demonstrations with people under stress, where I place an oxygen monitor on their finger and measure their oxygen before they focus on their breathing and afterwards. Almost always, after deep breathing, their oxygen saturation (percent of oxygen in their blood) goes up.

I will describe the entire meditation procedure, combining all the parts from the previous days.

– Choose a location that is dark and quiet. Turn off your pager and silence your cell phone. Sit on a comfortable chair, hands gently on your knees, or kneel on the floor with hands gently on your knees, or sit with legs crossed, forearms on thighs, and palms up. You should be perfectly comfortable and pain free.

– Gently close your eyes. Begin your slow rhythmic breaths, in through the nose and out through the mouth.

– As you inhale, feel the air moving through the back of your throat as your belly expands. As you draw in a breath through the back of your throat, feel your body expand, moving upward, and picture your lungs fully expanding as you fill up every last air pocket with oxygen throughout your lungs.

– At maximum inhalation, hold your breath for about a second. Then gradually, slowly let the air passively flow from the back of your throat, forcing out the last breath. Exhaling is typically slower than inhaling. In your mind, count as you inhale and work to double that count as you exhale. The exhaled breath should sound like a calm wind.

– As you exhale, have your mind say something like "calm" or "peace" as you picture the stress and negative thoughts leave your body. In your mind's eye, picture yourself walking down a hallway. Notice the floor beneath your feet. Notice the tiling on the ceiling. Notice the pictures on the wall.

– As you continue to walk, picture an elevator in the distance. Continue your breathing as you approach the elevator. As you face the elevator, watch the doors open. Go in. Turn and watch the doors close. All the while, continue your breathing—in through the nose and out through the mouth.

– As you picture yourself standing, facing the door, begin contracting individual muscles. Start with the toes. As you inhale, contract your toes. As you exhale, relax them. Next, as you inhale, contract your calves. As you exhale, relax them. Continue this as you move up your body, alternating your back and your front.

– In your mind, picture yourself with a big smile almost ready to break into a belly laugh. After you contract and relax your scalp (by lifting your eyebrows), you are ready for descent. As I said in previous days, if you feel uneasy about descending below an imaginary ground level, have yourself start on the tenth floor and descend from there, exiting at the ground level.

– I will describe the descent from the ground level, exiting at the tenth floor below ground. You can picture a digital floor display in the elevator, with the floor levels lit up as you pass them, and an arrow pointing downward. Each floor corresponds to a respiratory cycle.

– As you descend, continue your rhythmic breathing. As you reach the tenth floor, pause, and begin breathing in through your nose and out also through your nose. Continue breathing this way until you feel comfortable doing so.

– Stay in this place and understand that any fear or unease you may feel is coming from your AB trying to "protect" you from this dangerous and unpredictable place. As with all messages from the AB, the opposite is true: This place is safe and predictable.

– Do not try to have a particular experience. Do not predict what you might find. Do not try to meet Abe. Just allow the doors to open. You may see darkness. You may see a bright light. You may see a garden, or a meadow, as I did the first time. You may see absolutely nothing.

– Your AB may be active at times, even in this place. If you recall, the AB when activated by danger stimulates the release of hormones that make you feel nervous. But this effect lasts only briefly— unless you believe its warning. If you continue to breathe slowly and steadily, nervousness will pass and let you see your mind.

– On one occasion, I forgot to turn off my phone and the vibration of an incoming text message startled me. I felt my pulse quicken and my body begin to tremble. I continued my breathing, but made sure to inhale a little more deeply and exhale a little more completely, and the symptoms of the AB faded rapidly. I was again face to face with Abe, vividly, without distraction.

– I will not say much about your visit to this special place within your mind. Your experience will be highly personal. It is unique because it belongs to you, yet you will meet something that all of us possess.

– When your visit is complete, and you will sense it, then reenter the elevator, and travel upward to the ground floor (or the tenth floor, if that's where you started). As you travel upward, focus again on your breathing as you return to breathing in through your nose and out through your mouth. Each floor will be an inhale and exhale cycle, as you see the floors rise more rapidly.

As you practice and become more comfortable with meditation, you can begin asking open-ended questions. I would suggest not asking specific questions or trying to predict the future. Meditation is not a means to an end. It is a means to an awakening and a connection with your life force. This life force may be a liaison to God, or a portal to a greater essential energy. Or it can be simply tapping into the innate power of your mind. Whatever and however you define it, this life force that we reach by way of our mind is the source of what we need. It is important to trust that it will bring to us just that. When we ask for specific things, we doubt its power. When you are in your meditation, you will gain this feeling of trust and security.

I wrote in a weekly message about the time my mind (Abe) asked me what I really wanted. When I replied, "To have my book published," I instantly developed a disabling muscle spasm that jolted me out of meditation. Never before had this happened. After it subsided and I returned to my meditation, Abe asked me the same question: "What do you really want?" I replied:

"To believe 100 percent without reservation in Abe, or my mind, or God, or whatever. What I really want is to believe 100 percent that I can attract to my family and myself everything that is right for us. To believe 100 percent in something that transcends my five senses, but brings to me things that my five senses can appreciate. To believe 100 percent that my mind serves as the portal to a greater spiritual force that defies the physical world and the fear-based mechanics of the AB; to believe 100 percent in myself and my innate ability to connect with this force through the power of my mind; to believe 100 percent that every single individual has this innate power, the essence of who they are."

When I received this answer, I realized my book would not be complete until I added this third section. After all, if I do not believe 100 percent in myself and my work, who will really believe in me?

Many people espouse their belief publicly in the kind of metaphysical concepts described in *The Secret* or the Bible. But as we sit in our quietest moments and evaluate our lives, seeing things and feeling things that do not jibe with our public views, how does that discordance impact our beliefs—really? When believers scramble to be better believers than someone else, or intellectually battle one another, do they believe in the power of the mind or are they simply following the reflex of the AB to one-up each other?

As for me and this book, I know that whatever happens will happen the way it should happen. I do not know when, how, where, or in what shape or form. All I can be sure of is that whatever does happen, I will have Abe right there on my side, within me, and I know it will be right— not only for me but for all whom I reach with my words. That's what I can predict. That's what I can be sure of. And a few more things I can be sure of: *I believe 100 percent in my life, I believe 100 percent in my journey, and I am free.*

Acknowledgments

Thank you to all those who helped me on my journey. There are some, though, whom I would like to acknowledge separately.

I thank my parents Albert and Bernice Glassman for always believing in me, well before I learned to believe in myself.

When I expressed my interest in becoming a doctor, my high school advisor advised against it because medicine was a "very difficult field in which to break in." Little did I know, this would become a very strong example for me of an "external" automatic brain. I later determined not to believe, trust, or take direction from him. To be sure, in high school I was an average student—nowhere near the top of my class. Ironically this advisor's lack of belief in me helped me not to believe in my limitations and eventually learn to tap into the power of my mind.

I am fortunate to be surrounded by so many sincere friends and I am thankful to all for your support. I must give special thanks to my dear friend, Stuart Greenblatt, who for many months has been my "morning cup of coffee." Interspersed with belly-laughing humor, our conversations have served to clarify my teachings, self-knowledge, and understanding of the power of the mind. Stu, I appreciate your wisdom, genuineness and friendship.

When the inspiration came to me to turn my weekly messages into a book, Ken Franklin approached me to offer his editing expertise. After reviewing his sample editing of my first chapter, I was hooked! Thanks, Ken, for your skill and attention.

Thank you, Jill Little, for your skillful design work. Thank you, Etty Faskha for your artistic ideas.

Eva Kramer has been my office manager since I started my new practice. Eva, thanks for your passion, dedication, and encouragement.

Thank you to my patients for your continued belief and trust in my work and allowing me into your lives to share it.

I am especially blessed with four phenomenal and spectacular children: Zachary, Jeremy, Samantha, and Danielle. Your individual special qualities are a daily reminder of the magic of life.

My wife Melanie has always supported my dreams and has been patient whenever my automatic brain slips into the mix. I thank you, Melanie, for your love, guidance, wisdom, and support.

My inner guide has directed me along a path that just keeps getting more exciting. Every single chapter started with inspiration given to me during meditation, when I am able to connect with my inner sage. Thank you, Abe, for being my reliable guide, in whom I can believe and trust.

About the Author

Charles F. Glassman, MD, FACP, graduated Phi Beta Kappa, magna cum laude, from Hobart College in Geneva, NY. He received his MD degree from New York Medical College in Valhalla, NY. Dr. Glassman served an internship in General Surgery at the Albert Einstein School of Medicine affiliated hospitals in The Bronx, New York, and completed his residency training in internal medicine at Westchester Medical Center, Valhalla, NY. For the past 21 years, Dr. Glassman has practiced general internal medicine in Rockland County, a suburban community 30 miles north of New York City, designing his practice to be patient-centered instead of problem-focused.

He has appeared on ABC news, Bloomberg Radio, National Public Radio, and The Wall Street Journal Radio, speaking on his unique approach to health care. Dr. Glassman's numerous articles and letters on health care have appeared in The New York Times and other publications.

Mindful of the limitations of conventional medicine, Dr. Glassman has been able to integrate alternative practices to bring his patients the best potential for health and longevity. In 2005, Dr. Glassman founded the New York Center for Longevity and Wellness. The goal of the Center is to balance mind-body concepts with conventional medicine to deliver a comprehensive approach to health and wellness. Since the Center opened, Dr. Glassman has been featured in many local publications, notably the regional Hudson Valley Magazine, which has repeatedly named him one of the top doctors in the Hudson Valley (spanning an area from Albany to

New York City). In addition to appearing as the subject of feature-length articles, Dr. Glassman has been named by Castle Connolly as a New York Metro Top Doctor for five consecutive years and has been recognized by the Consumers' Research Council of America as one of America's top physicians.

Dr. Glassman began distributing a weekly motivational email message to patients and friends in January 2007. By May 2008, his distribution list had grown so much—as people on the list told others about it—and interest in his messages had become so high—Dr. Glassman decided to turn his philosophy and advice into a book. That's how *Brain Drain* came about. Starting in May 2008, his weekly messages—now distributed to an even larger audience—formed the basis for chapters of this book.

Dr. Glassman lives in Rockland County, NY with his wife Melanie and their four children (and dog, Ginger).